225a

COLLEGE PHYSICS

COLLEGE PHYSICS

Volume I

MECHANICS, WAVE MOTION, SOUND

Robert L. Weber

Associate Professor of Physics

The Pennsylvania State University

Englewood Cliffs, N.J.

PRENTICE-HALL, INC.

1958

Library of Congress Catalog Card Number: 58-11215

Printed in the United States of America

14803

Preface

This is not a textbook or a substitute for a textbook. *College Physics* is designed to help you recognize and master the essential ideas of physics, to develop facility in the solution of problems, and to succeed in writing a good examination—a sort of "How-to-do-it" book in physics.

College Physics is chiefly a review outline of general physics, and a collection of questions which have appeared on recent tests and final examinations in introductory college physics courses.

The idea of assembling examination questions for review purpose is not new; the Library of Congress catalog lists some eighteen books which are such collections. *College Physics* differs from these in some or all of the following features:

1. The brief outline of physical principles is planned to aid a student in acquiring a mature understanding of the topics included in most beginning courses in college physics, including *atomic and nuclear physics.*

2. In Mechanics, emphasis is on the more familiar British (gravitational) system of units. The metric absolute systems are used where necessary as a basis for the units that are commonly met in science. (The British absolute and the metric gravitational systems are *not* used in this book.) In Electricity, rationalized mks units are used. Magnetic properties and units are developed in the spirit of the mks system, and not in terms of fictitious isolated magnetic poles.

3. Over 150 completely solved problems are included in the text to illustrate calculations based on the more important physical concepts and principles.

4. A great many questions, graded in difficulty, are presented for the student's use in developing a mastery of physics that comes from problem solving. Every question in *College Physics* has appeared on recent test or examination papers, though some have been edited in accord with (2).

5. Questions have been arranged by topics in the various chapters, to facilitate their use with current assignments.

6. In addition, there are complete sample tests and examinations for review of an entire semester's work, and for "time trials" in developing confidence in taking examinations.

7. The numerical problems in *College Physics* have been selected from the author's files and from some 5000 questions collected for this book from some 50 colleges and universities. Thus this problem collection is representative of the general college physics course.

8. A glance at the Contents will show many other aids in making your study of physics more systematic, more interesting, and more fruitful.

Robert L. Weber

The Pennsylvania State University
  University Park, Pa.

Acknowledgments

To all who have contributed advice and sample problems to the three volumes comprising *College Physics Review* I express thanks. Especially, I want to acknowledge the help of the following, who contributed examination material (and in some cases entire course outlines):

Dr. R. Stanley Alexander, Crane Observatory, Washburn University
Prof. Roy S. Anderson, University of Maryland
Prof. Yardley Beers, New York University
Prof. Robert A. Boyer, Muhlenberg College
Prof. Sherwood B. Brown, Colby College
Dr. L. L. Chapin, Registrar, National Bureau of Standards Graduate School
Prof. H. H. Classen, Wheaton College
Prof. Roy M. Dibert, Shippensburg State Teachers College, Pa.
Prof. Samuel H. Dwight, Michigan State College
Prof. John A. Eldridge, University of Iowa
Prof. W. H. Eller, Western Illinois State College
Prof. Arnold M. Flikke, University of Minnesota
Prof. Ira Freeman, Rutgers University
Prof. Harold Q. Fuller, Missouri School of Mines and Metallurgy
Prof. G. E. Grantham, Cornell University
Prof. Michael Grandy, University of Dayton, Ohio
Prof. W. E. Haisley, Brown University
Prof. Lloyd B. Ham, University of Arkansas
Prof. Milton D. Hare, Union College, Lincoln, Nebraska
Prof. Clement L. Henshaw, Colgate University
Prof. Claude W. Horton, University of Texas
Prof. Gordon F. Hull, Jr., Dartmouth College
Prof. A. Leitner, Michigan State College
Prof. Tate J. Lindsey, University of South Carolina
Prof. Arthur Lutz, Wittenberg College
Prof. Walter H. Mais, Brooklyn College
Sister Mary Robert, Trinity College, Washington, D. C.
Prof. R. F. McCune, Bucknell University
Prof. Charles S. Morris, Manchester College, North Manchester, Ind.
Prof. Robert W. Morse, Brown University
Dr. Elmer Nussbaum, University of Rochester
Prof. Robert Petry, University of the South
Dr. Israel Rotkin, National Bureau of Standards Graduate School
Prof. Raymond J. Seeger, National Science Foundation
Prof. Paul E. Shearin, University of North Carolina
Prof. W. W. Sleator, University of Michigan (retired)

Prof. Clarence R. Smith, Aurora College
Prof. Kenneth Steele, Tri-State College, Angola, Ind.
Prof. Edward C. Stevenson, University of Virginia
Prof. J. G. Stipe, Randolph-Macon Woman's College
Prof. Foster Strong, California Institute of Technology
Prof. Francis E. Throw, Wabash College
Prof. C. W. Ufford, University of Pennsylvania
Prof. H. R. Voorhees, University of Chicago
Prof. G. L. Weissler, University of Southern California, Los Angeles
Prof. Harvey E. White, University of California, Berkeley
Prof. Roy V. Wiegand, Montana State College
Prof. Douglas B. Williamson, West Virginia University

Contents

Part I. MECHANICS

Part II. WAVE MOTION; SOUND

Part I

MECHANICS

CHAPTER 1

Introduction to the Study of Physics;
Mathematical Preliminaries

A *science* is a body of knowledge which is organized, experimentally verifiable, and which is fruitful in the search for more knowledge. In the development of a science, essential steps have been: observation, recording, analysis, prediction, and verification. *Physics* is the science of matter and energy. Physics deals with mechanics, heat, sound, light, electricity and magnetism, and atomic and nuclear processes.

How to Study Physics

Find out the objective of the course of study you are undertaking. The Catalog may give you a hint. Your instructor will be glad to elaborate.

Get a loose-leaf notebook, preferably for $8\frac{1}{2} \times 11$ inch sheets. Arrange in it an orderly file of printed lecture notes, solutions to assigned problems, the notes you take in class, tests and examinations.

In preparing a new topic, first read the textbook assignment rapidly, to get the gist of it. Then go back and write a brief outline of important physical principles, definitions of terms new to you, and what appear to be important equations. If your textbook provides a chapter Summary, check your outline with it. Make sure that you understand the reasoning in any mathematical derivations, and that you are aware of any simplifying assumptions which limit the application of the resulting equation. Then attack the numerical problems which are part of your assignment.

Study regularly.

In the demonstration lectures, in your reading, and in laboratory manipulation, keep your attention on *physical principles*, rather than exclusively on gadgets or displays. Particular instruments or methods of measurement may become obsolete, but if you have an understanding of the basic physical principles involved, you will be able to extend them to new situations.

Look for relationships between new laws and new methods and the ones already familiar. (How is Lenz's law related to the principle of the conservation of energy? Why do we encounter "inverse square" laws in light, magnetism, electrostatics, and gravitation?)

The best test of your grasp of physics is your ability to *use* its principles. In an academic sense, this usually means facility in solving problems.

For additional study suggestions, many of which you will want to adopt, see: Chapman, S., *How to Study Physics* (1949). Addison-Wesley Publishing Co., Inc., Reading, Mass. (33 pp.).

How to Find Information in Physics Literature

Do you feel lost in a technical library? Would you have difficulty in planning a summer's reading in the history of physics, or in biophysics? or in finding the latest characteristics of "certain" and "probable" mesons and hyperons? or the titles of interesting motion picture films in nuclear physics? Then the two books listed below should be valuable guides.

The first, *Physics Literature*, is especially neatly arranged to answer inquiries from a variety of approaches: bibliographical, historical, biographical, experimental, mathematical, educational, terminological, and topical. This reference manual describes the many kinds of physics literature. It outlines effective library methods. It selects and gives a classified list of a representative working collection. And although essentially bibliographical, it is itself pleasant reading.

Whitford, Robert H., *Physics Literature, A Reference Manual* (1954). The Scarecrow Press, Box 1855, New Brunswick, N. J. (228 pp.).

Parke, Nathan G., *Guide to the Literature of Mathematics and Physics, Including Related Works in Engineering Science* (1947). The McGraw-Hill Book Co., Inc., New York (205 pp.).

How to Solve Physical Problems

The ability to solve problems is a mark of an effective and efficient scientist or engineer. Through practice in the solution of problems commensurate with one's knowledge, one attains ability and confidence in independent thinking.

In problem solving, the following systematic approach is highly recommended. First, read the statement of the problem carefully, and decide exactly what is required. Then:

1. Draw a suitable diagram, and list the data given.
2. Identify the type of problem, and write physical principles which

seem relevant to its solution.   These may be expressed concisely in algebraic equations.

3. Determine whether or not the data given are adequate. If not, decide what is missing and how to get it. This may require consulting a table, making a reasonable assumption, or drawing upon your general knowledge for such information as the value of "g," the acceleration due to gravity (32 ft/sec²).

4. Decide whether in the particular problem it is easier to substitute numerical values immediately, or first to carry out an algebraic solution. In the latter case, some "unknown" quantities may cancel.

5. Substitute numerical data in the equations obtained from physical principles. Include the units for each quantity; make sure that they are all in the same system of units in any one problem.

6. Compute the numerical value of the "unknown," preferably with the aid of a slide rule. Determine the units in which the answer is expressed. Examine the reasonableness of the answer. (If you have computed the cost of operating a small electrical appliance for 8 hr as $2.4 million, check your arithmetic.) If possible, obtain the answer by an alternative method to check your result.

An orderly procedure such as that outlined above aids clear thinking, helps avoid errors, and usually saves time.   Most important, having a *plan* enables you to analyze and eventually to solve those more complex problems whose solution is not immediately or intuitively apparent.

How to Improve Your Laboratory Reports

Your Laboratory Reports may be improved by following this list of general suggestions about their format (or the specific suggestions given to you by your instructor). You may want to take one of your completed reports and check it against this list.

( ) 1. Give completely the information requested in the printed heading of the Laboratory Report form.

( ) 2. Be neat. Have a plan in mind before you record data. Record the data directly in final form, not on scratch paper.

( ) 3. List data in tabular form. The headings should show clearly the quantities measured and the units used. Record the *original* measurements. (If you require the cross-sectional area of a cylindrical rod, record the measured diameter, not just your calculated value of $\pi d^2/4$, which may contain an arithmetical error.)

( ) 4. Always include the original data sheet with your Report, even though it may have been rewritten for neatness.

( ) 5. Record data to the proper number of significant figures.

( ) 6. For each type of computation made from your data, show one sample calculation in detail, including the proper units. For repeated calculations, only the results need be listed.

( ) 7. Follow accepted rules for retaining the proper number of significant figures in a result computed from experimental data. State the uncertainty in your computed result.

( ) 8. If you have access to a "standard value," in a Handbook or elsewhere, compute the error in your final result. (Error = Observed value − Accepted value.) If the actual error exceeds the uncertainty claimed, explain.

( ) 9. Give each graph an *informative* title. For example, "Pressure of Saturated Water Vapor vs. Temperature" is more informative than a cryptic "*P* vs *T*."

( ) 10. Label the axes of a graph, stating what is being plotted, and in what units.

( ) 11. Indicate experimental points on a graph (preferably as tiny circles) and draw the smooth curve of best fit through the experimental points.

In writing the Conclusions to your experiment, stress: (a) significance of the experiment, (b) final numerical results, and (c) the degree of accuracy (% uncertainty) of these results.

( ) 12. In the Conclusion, state first the *significance* of the experiment. Put the most general and important statements first. What principle has been verified, or what physical quantity has been measured? (If in doubt, reread what you have stated as the *Object* of the experiment. Has it been fulfilled?)

( ) 13. List final numerical results only (the average value, if you have made several "runs"). Include the proper number of significant figures. State the units in which the answer is expressed.

( ) 14. If you can calculate the error in your result, do so. Otherwise indicate the reliability of the result by the number of significant figures used to express it, and state the estimated uncertainty.

( ) 15. When results are presented in graphical form, interpret the significance of the relationship shown in the graph. (Choose the scale for plotting a graph to display your data to the best advantage. For example, if the slope of a straight-line relationship is sought, a graph scaled to give a line at about 45° to the *x*-axis is better than one giving a 5° line.)

( ) 16. Discuss the accuracy of your results. Mention sources of error in order of probable importance, and state any special precautions you took to reduce errors.

The experiments performed as part of a basic physics course usually differ considerably in the accuracy obtainable. In judging your Report, the emphasis is not chiefly on small error, but rather on your ability to make a reasonable estimate of the accuracy attainable with the instruments and method actually used.

( ) 17. Optional: Where appropriate, compare the method or instruments used in the experiment with others known to you, as to accuracy, convenience, etc.

In handling uncertainties of measurement, follow the procedures prescribed for your course by your instructor, or consult:

Beers, Yardley, *Introduction to the Theory of Error*, 2d ed. (1957). Addison-Wesley Publishing Co., Inc., Reading, Mass. (66 pp.).

Wall, C. N., and R. B. Levine, *Physics Laboratory Manual*, pp. 1–6 (1951) Prentice-Hall, Inc., Englewood Cliffs, N. J. (232 pp.).

How to Review for an Examination...

1. Read the summaries you have made in your notes of the important ideas in each chapter of your textbook, or the chapter summaries given in the textbook.

2. Make sure that each equation expressing an important relation or principle has physical meaning for you, and that you are aware of any limitations in its application.

3. From your earlier test papers and homework, select those problems which caused you difficulty. Correct them or complete them. For each, find a problem on the same topic in your textbook or in this booklet and make sure that you now understand the topic by at least setting up the working equation and an indicated solution for the problem.

4. Now look through sample examination questions to find (a) any "blind spots" (topics you may have missed in your study and review) and (b) any problems for which you do not immediately see a method of solution. Work on these with the aid of your textbook or other help.

5. Finally, if you are one who feels rushed during an examination, select a specimen examination (there are some in this booklet) and write out a complete set of answers, allowing yourself no more time than that specified for the examination. This practice should build your speed and self-confidence.

...and How to Write an Examination

1. Listen to and read carefully any preliminary Directions, and heed them!

In the specimen tests collected in this booklet, the Directions have been omitted in many cases to save space. In general, they were worded something like this:

"Write your name and that of your instructor on the front cover of your examination booklet. Begin your answer to each of the numbered questions at the top of a new page. Clearly indicate the method of solution for numerical problems: (a) write the working equation in symbolic form, (b) substitute the numerical data, and (c) solve for a numerical answer, with proper units and the correct number of significant figures. No credit will be given for a numerical answer alone."

2. Read each question carefully, so that you are sure what is required.

3. Try to make at least a start in the solution of every problem, following the outline given above. Generally a correctly indicated solution will receive almost full credit, even if you do not have time to complete the arithmetic.

4. If the test is a multiple-choice type, be sure you understand the basis of grading. Will the score be (a) the number of correct answers or (b) the number of correct answers minus $(1/n)$(number of wrong answers)? In case (a), it is obviously to your advantage to answer every question, even if some guessing is needed. In case (b), it may be better to leave unanswered any questions about which you feel you have no information.

Measurement

Measurement means comparing a thing with a standard to see how many times as large it is. Three *fundamental quantities* are necessary in mechanics. These are commonly chosen as *length, mass*, and *time* (or as *length, force*, and *time*). For each fundamental quantity, there is an arbitrarily chosen *fundamental unit* (e.g., for length, the meter). Other units based on fundamental units are called *derived units* (e.g., for speed, the meter/second).

In the United States, our units are defined in terms of metric standards. A complete set of units, both fundamental and derived, is called a *system of units*. Systems of units are named from the fundamental units used as basic for the system: fps (foot-pound-second), cgs (centimeter-gram-second), and mks (meter-kilogram-second). Only a few conversion factors are needed to convert all derived units from one system to another. Many additional conversion relations are given in the Appendix, for convenience in numerical computations.

1 meter = 100 centimeters = 39.37 inches

1 inch = 2.540 centimeters

1 kilogram = 100 grams = 2.205 pounds

Mathematical Preliminaries

1. Formulas from geometry. Here r denotes radius, h altitude, B area of base, s slant height, and a, b, c, the semiaxes of an ellipse or ellipsoid.

1. Circumference of a circle $= 2\pi r$. Arc of sector $= r\theta$ (θ in radians).
2. Area of circle $= \pi r^2$. Area of sector $= (1/2) r^2 \theta$ (θ in radians).
3. Volume of prism $= Bh$.
4. Volume of right circular cylinder $= \pi r^2 h$.
5. Lateral surface of right circular cylinder $= 2\pi rh$.
6. Total surface of right circular cylinder $= 2\pi r(r + h)$.
7. Volume of right circular cone $= (1/3)\pi r^2 h$.
8. Lateral surface of right circular cone $= \pi rs$.
9. Volume of sphere $= (4/3)\pi r^2$.
10. Surface of sphere $= 4\pi r^2$.
11. Area of ellipse $= \pi ab$.
12. Volume of ellipsoid $= (4/3)\pi abc$.

2. Relations from trigonometry. In the study of vectors, especially, the following simple trigonometric relations are very useful.

(a) *Right triangle* ($C = 90°$):

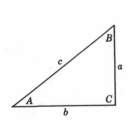

$$\sin A = \frac{a}{c} \qquad \sin B = \frac{b}{c}$$

$$\cos A = \frac{b}{c} \qquad \cos B = \frac{a}{c}$$

$$\tan A = \frac{a}{b} \qquad \tan B = \frac{b}{a}$$

$$\sin A = \cos B$$

(b) *Any triangle:*

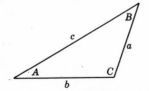

Law of sines:

$$\frac{a}{\sin A} = \frac{b}{\sin B} = \frac{c}{\sin C}$$

Law of cosines:

$$c^2 = a^2 + b^2 - 2ab \cos C$$

(c) *Trigonometric formulas:*

$$\sin^2 A + \cos^2 A = 1$$

$$\sin (A + B) = \sin A \cos B + \cos A \sin B$$

$$\cos (A + B) = \cos A \cos B + \sin A \sin B$$

$$\tan A = \frac{\sin A}{\cos A}$$

(d) *Approximations for small angles:*

$$\sin A = \tan A = A \text{ (in radians)}$$

3. **Formulas from calculus.** Here u, v, and w are variables which are functions of x; c and n are constants.

(a) *Differentiation:*

1. $\dfrac{dc}{dx} = 0$

2. $\dfrac{dx}{dx} = 1$

3. $\dfrac{d}{dx} (u + v - w) = \dfrac{du}{dx} + \dfrac{dv}{dx} - \dfrac{dw}{dx}$

4. $\dfrac{d}{dx} cv = c \dfrac{dv}{dx}$

5. $\dfrac{d}{dx} uv = u \dfrac{dv}{dx} + v \dfrac{du}{dx}$

6. $\dfrac{d}{dx} x^n = nx^{n-1}$

7. $\dfrac{d}{dx} v^n = nv^{n-1} \dfrac{dv}{dx}$

8. $\dfrac{d}{dx} \dfrac{u}{v} = \dfrac{v (du/dx) - u (dv/dx)}{v^2}$

9. $\dfrac{d}{dx} \sin u = \cos u \dfrac{du}{dx}$

10. $\dfrac{d}{dx} \cos u = -\sin u \dfrac{du}{dx}$

(b) *Integration:*

11. $\displaystyle\int \dfrac{du}{u} = \ln u + c$

12. $\displaystyle\int \sin u \; du = -\cos u + c$

13. $\displaystyle\int \cos u \; du = \sin u + c$

4. Greek alphabet.

A	α	alpha	N	ν	nu
B	β	beta	Ξ	ξ	xi
Γ	γ	gamma	O	o	omicron
Δ	δ	delta	Π	π	pi
E	ϵ	epsilon	P	ρ	rho
Z	ζ	zeta	Σ	σ	sigma
H	η	eta	T	τ	tau
Θ	θ	theta	Υ	υ	upsilon
I	ι	iota	Φ	φ	phi .
K	κ	kappa	X	χ	chi
Λ	λ	lambda	Ψ	ψ	psi
M	μ	mu	Ω	ω	omega

5. Symbols.

$=$ means equal to

$\equiv$ means is defined as, or is identical to

$\neq$ means is not equal to

$\propto$ means varies as, or is proportional to

Σ means the sum of

$\bar{x}$ means average value of x

$\doteq$ means is approximately equal to

$>$ means is greater than ($\gg$ means much greater than)

$<$ means less than ($\ll$ means much less than)

$^-$vinculum (bar over digit) indicates first doubtful digit, e.g., $12,\overline{6}00$ is stated to only three significant figures

6. Brief instructions on use of a slide rule.*

How to Multiply. Multiplication is generally performed on the "C" and "D" scales. The number "1" on the left end of the scale is called the "Left Index," and the number "1" at the right end of the scale is called the "Right Index."

---

*Instructions and copyright illustrations courtesy of Eugene Dietzgen Co.

Rule for multiplication: Set index of "C" scale over either of the factors on the "D" scale. Move the hairline on the indicator to the second factor on the "C" scale. Read the answer on the "D" scale, under the hairline. Determine the location of the decimal point by a rough mental approximation.

Example: Multiply 17 × 23. See Fig. 1-1.

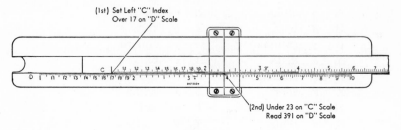

Fig. 1-1

How to Divide. Division is generally performed on the "C" and "D" scales also.

Rule for division: Set the hairline over the numerator (dividend) on the "D" scale and bring the denominator (divisor) on the "C" scale under the hairline. Read the answer on the "D" scale, under the index of the "C" scale. Determine the decimal point by rough mental approximation.

Example: Divide 6 by 3. See Fig. 1-2.

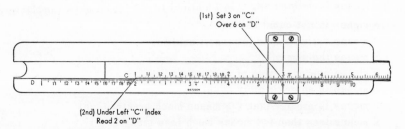

Fig. 1-2

How to Find a Square Root. Problems involving square roots are worked on the "A" and "B" scales in conjunction with the "C" and "D" scales. Note that the "A" and "B" scales are divided into two identical parts, which will be referred to as "A-left" and "A-right."

Rule for square roots: If the number is greater than unity, and has an odd number of figures before the decimal point, set the hairline over the number on "A-left" and read the square root under the hairline on the "D" scale. If the number has an even number of figures before the decimal point, use "A-right" instead of "A-left." Locate the decimal point in the answer by mental approximation.

If the number is less than unity, move the decimal point an *even* number of places to the right until a number between 1 and 100 is obtained. Find the square root of the number thus obtained as explained above. To locate the decimal point, move it to the left one-half as many places as it was originally moved to the right.

Example: Find the square root of 567. See Fig. 1-3.

Use "A-left," since there is an odd number of figures before the decimal point. By mental approximation, locate the decimal point after the second significant figure, making the answer 23.8.

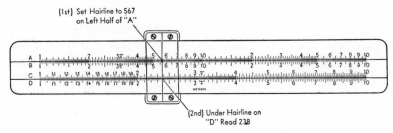

Fig. 1-3

Example: Find the square root of 0.0956. See Fig. 1-4.

Move the decimal point two places to the right, thus obtaining 9.56. Use the "A-left," because there is now an odd number of figures before the decimal point. Take the square root of 9.56, then move the decimal point *one* place to the left, making the answer 0.309.

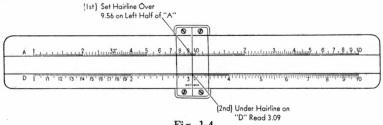

Fig. 1-4

CHAPTER 2

Vectors; Forces at a Point

A *vector quantity* is a quantity whose measurement is specified by magnitude and direction. Examples are displacement, velocity, force, acceleration, and momentum. A vector quantity is represented graphically by an arrow-directed line called a *vector* drawn to represent its direction and its magnitude on some convenient scale.

A *scalar quantity* has only magnitude. Examples are time, mass, energy, and volume.

The *resultant* of two or more vectors is the single vector that would have the same effect.

In the *parallelogram* method of vector addition (Fig. 2-1), the resultant R is conveniently found from the law of cosines and the law of sines.

$$R^2 = A^2 + B^2 + 2AB \cos \theta, \tag{2-1}$$

$$\frac{\sin \theta}{A} = \frac{\sin (180° - \theta)}{R}. \tag{2-2}$$

In the *vector polygon* method of vector addition, vectors are added graphically by placing them "head to tail" and drawing the resultant from

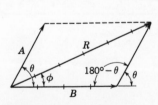

Fig. 2-1. Parallelogram method of vector addition.

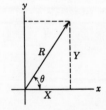

Fig. 2-2. Rectangular components.

the origin to the head of the last vector, closing the polygon.

The *rectangular components* of a vector (Fig. 2-2) are its projections on a set of right-angle axes, for example, the horizontal and vertical axes.

$$X = R \cos \theta, \tag{2-3}$$

$$Y = R \sin \theta. \tag{2-4}$$

In the *component* method of vector addition, each vector is resolved into its rectangular components. These are added algebraically and the resultant found:

$$R^2 = (\Sigma \ X)^2 + (\Sigma \ Y)^2. \tag{2-5}$$

Here $\Sigma \ X$ means the sum of the components along the x-axis; $\Sigma \ Y$ means the sum of the components along the y-axis.

A body is in *equilibrium* when there is no change in its motion. A body is in translational equilibrium when it is at rest or is moving in a straight line with constant speed. A body is in rotational equilibrium when it is at rest or is rotating about a fixed axis with a constant angular speed.

First condition for equilibrium. When a body is in equilibrium, the vector sum of all the forces acting on it is zero. The vector diagram is a closed polygon. The sums of the rectangular components of all the forces must each equal zero:

$$\Sigma \ F_x = 0 \quad \text{and} \quad \Sigma \ F_y = 0. \tag{2-6}$$

Example: Add vectors of 7.0 units and 4.0 units making an angle of 60° with each other.

On a convenient scale, draw vectors A and B, making an angle of 60° from a common origin, O (Fig. 2-3). Complete the parallelogram with A and B as sides and draw the diagonal from O, placing an arrowhead at the end of R. On the scale selected, R represents the resultant of 9.6 units at an angle of 21° with A.

The resultant may also be determined analytically from the cosine law:

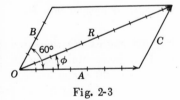

Fig. 2-3

$$R^2 = A^2 + B^2 + 2AB \cos 60°,$$

$$R^2 = 49 + 16 + 2\,(7.0)\,(4.0)\,(0.50) = 93,$$

$$R = 9.6 \text{ units.}$$

The angle ϕ may be determined from the sine law:

$$\frac{R}{\sin 120°} = \frac{C}{\sin \phi},$$

$$\sin \phi = \frac{C}{R} \sin 120° = \frac{4.0}{9.6} \times 0.87 = 0.3\overline{6}3;$$

hence

$$\text{angle } \phi = 21°.$$

Example: Find the sum of the following displacements: 3.50 mi east, 12.00 mi 30.0° N of E, and 4.00 mi 60.0° S of W (Fig. 2-4).

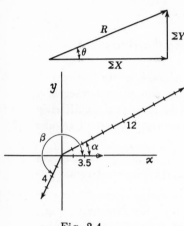

$$\alpha = 30° \quad \text{and} \quad \beta = 240°,$$

$$\sin \alpha = 0.500, \qquad \sin \beta = -0.866,$$

$$\cos \alpha = 0.866, \qquad \cos \beta = -0.500.$$

$$\Sigma X = 3.50 + 12.00 (0.866) + 4.00 (-0.500)$$
$$= 11.90,$$

$$\Sigma Y = 0 + 12.00 (0.500) + 4.00 (-0.866)$$
$$= 2.54,$$

$$R^2 = 10.90^2 + 2.54^2 = 125,$$

$$R = 11.2 \text{ mi},$$

$$\tan \theta = 2.54/10.90, \qquad \theta = 13.1°.$$

Fig. 2-4

Note that a vector has no component at right angles to itself: the 3.5-mi vector has no y-component. Note also that the sign of a component can be determined either by the sign of a trigonometric function or by inspection of the diagram.

PROBLEMS

Vector components

2-1. Is it possible to have more than one pair of components for a given force? Explain.

2-2. In the following three problems, direction angles are measured counterclockwise from the positive x-axis. Find the horizontal and vertical components of each of the following forces: (a) 100 dynes at 30°, (b) 20 lb at 140°, (c) 300 dynes at 200°, (d) 200 newtons at 0° (e) 5 poundals at 270°, (f) 2 lb at 350°, (g) 50 poundals at 90° (h) 40 newtons at 70° (i) 30 lb at 180°, (j) 20 dynes at 260°.

2-3. For each force in Problem 2-2, find the components respectively parallel and perpendicular to the line L_1 in Fig. 2-5. (Ans: (a) 98.5, 17.4 dynes; (e) −1.71, −0.47 poundal)

2-4. For each force in Problem 2-2, find the components respectively parallel and perpendicular to the line L_2 in Fig. 2-6.

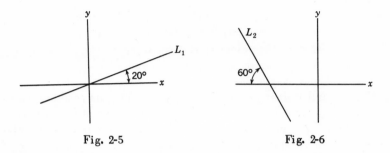

Fig. 2-5   Fig. 2-6

Vector resultants

2-5. Find the resultant (magnitude and direction) of each of the following sets of vectors, both graphically and by the method of components: (a) 1.0 lb at 20°, 2.0 lb at 90°, and 3.0 lb at 150°. (b) 200 dynes at 0°, 500 dynes at 180°, and 100 dynes at 220°. (c) 50 poundals at 270°, 20 poundals at 30°, and 10 poundals at 130°. (d) 100 newtons at 10°, 200 newtons at 20°, and 300 newtons at 30°. (e) 10 lb at 30°, 20 lb at 10°, 30 lb at 190°, and 40 lb at 300°. (*Ans:* (a) 4.2 lb at 113°)

2-6. Given two vectors: $A = 100$ units north, $B = 200$ units east. Show (rough sketch) how to obtain (a) the sum of A and B, (b) the difference $A - B$.

Displacement vectors

2-7. A man walks 3.0 mi directly northeast, then 2.0 mi east, and finally 1.0 mi southwest. (a) How many miles did he walk? (b) Specify the x- and y-coordinates of his final position with respect to the starting point. (c) What is the shortest distance from his starting point to the final position? (*Ans:* 6.0 mi; 3.4, 1.4; 3.7 mi)

2-8. A man walks 4.0 mi 37° north of east, then 2.0 mi east, and finally 3.0 mi south. (a) What distance has he walked? (b) What is his displacement with respect to the starting point?

2-9. A taxi driver averages 30 mi/hr. After traveling east for 1.0 hr he turns and drives north for 1.0 hr, then east again for 20 min. How far is he from the starting point? (*Ans:* 50 mi, 37° N of E)

Velocity vectors

2-10. A river is 3.0 mi wide and flows 4.0 mi/hr. A man can row 5.0 mi/hr in still water. (a) How long will it take him to row three miles down river and back? (b) How long will it take him to row straight across the river and back?

2-11. A pilot with a plane having a cruising speed of 200 mi/hr wishes to fly to another airport 100 mi to the north, and return. A steady wind of 50 mi/hr is blowing from the south. What is his total flying time in minutes for the round trip? (*Ans:* 55 min)

2-12. A river flows due north with a speed of 3.0 mi/hr. A man rows a boat across the river; his velocity relative to the water is 4.0 mi/hr, due east. (a) What is his velocity relative to the earth? (b) If the river is 2.0 mi wide, how far north of his starting point will he reach the opposite bank? (c) How long a time is required to cross the river?

2-13. A small trainer plane flies due east (compass reading) with an indicated air speed of 80 mi/hr. CAA reports the wind at this altitude to be 40 mi/hr toward 30° east of north. In what direction is the plane traveling? What length of time will be required for the plane to go 100 mi in this direction? (*Ans:* 10° N of E; 51 min)

Vectors, concurrent forces

2-14. The following four concurrent forces are in equilibrium: 10 lb toward east, 20 lb toward south, 30 lb 60° N of W, and force *E*. (a) Find *E* (both magnitude and direction). (b) Find the resultant of the first three forces.

2-15. A 100-lb body is suspended from the ceiling of a room by two ropes *A* and *B*. Rope *A* makes an angle of 30.0° with the horizontal and rope *B* makes an angle of 60.0° with the horizontal. Compute the tension in each rope. (*Ans:* 50.0 lb; 86.6 lb)

2-16. A 200-lb body is hung from the middle point of a horizontal wire which is 20.0 ft long. The wire stretches until the middle part sags 1.50 ft. (a) How much did the wire stretch? (b) What is the tension in the wire?

2-17. A rope 17.0 ft long has its ends attached to two points 13.0 ft apart in the ceiling of a room. If the maximum tension which the rope can withstand is 200 lb, what is the heaviest weight which can be suspended from a point 5.00 ft from one end of the rope? (Note: a 5-12-13 triangle is a right triangle.) (*Ans:* 459 lb)

2-18. A 400-lb block rests on a frictionless plane inclined at 30° to the horizontal. What force parallel to the plane is required to hold it stationary? Give the magnitudes and directions of *all* other forces acting on the block.

2-19. In the arrangement diagrammed in Fig. 2-7, *W* = 40.0 lb. Find tensions *F* and *S*. (*Ans:* 20.0 lb, 34.6 lb)

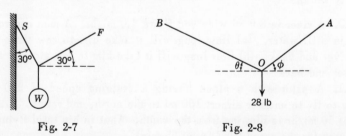

Fig. 2-7   Fig. 2-8

2-20. A rope *AOB* is used to suspend a 28-lb body at *O* in Fig. 2-8.

Given $\tan \theta = 5/12$; $\tan \phi = 3/4$. Find the tension in OA and in OB.

2-21. A 120-lb sphere rests in a V-shaped trough whose sides form an angle of 60° (Fig. 2-9). What is the normal force exerted by the sphere on each side of the trough? (*Ans:* 120 lb)

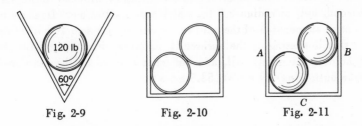

Fig. 2-9   Fig. 2-10   Fig. 2-11

2-22. Two identical smooth cylinders, each weighing 100 lb, are placed lengthwise in a narrow rectangular box (Fig. 2-10) whose width is three times the radius of the cylinders. Find (a) the force exerted by the bottom of the box on the lower of the two cylinders, (b) the force exerted by one cylinder on the other, and (c) the forces of the vertical walls on the cylinders. (*Ans:* 200 lb, 142 lb, 100 lb)

2-23. Two smooth identical spheres, each of weight W and radius r are resting in a smooth-sided slot of width $2\sqrt{3}\,r$, as in Fig. 2-11. Find the forces exerted by the walls on the spheres at the points A, B, and C. (*Ans:* $F_A = F_B = 1.07W$; $F_C = 2W$)

2-24. Four smooth solid balls are stacked on a smooth table in a pyramid, as in Fig. 2-12. The three bottom balls each have a radius of 5.0 in., and the top ball a radius of 8.0 in. The balls all have the same density, $0.54/\pi$ lb/in.^{3}. If the bottom balls are kept from moving by three straight wires running from center to center through radial holes, as shown, what is the tension in each wire? (*Ans:* 36 lb)

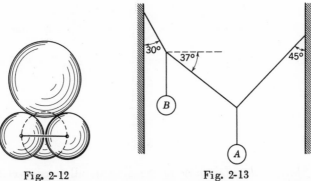

Fig. 2-12   Fig. 2-13

2-25. Two bodies, A and B, are hung from a rope which is attached at its ends to vertical walls, as in Fig. 2-13. If body A weighs 140 lb, find the weight of body B. (*Ans:* 79 lb)

2-26. A kite weighs 0.10 lb. The kite string makes an angle of 30° with the horizontal. The tension in the string is 0.30 lb. What is the direction and the magnitude of the force of the wind on the kite?

2-27. A string 10.0 in. long is fastened to a point 21.0 in. above a horizontal surface. The other end of the string is attached to the surface of a smooth ball of radius 2.0 in. which weighs 100 gm. Directly under the point of suspension of the cord is the center of a smooth ball of radius 6.0 in. that is resting on the surface (Fig. 2-14). Find the tension in the string holding the small ball, and the force exerted by the small ball on the large ball. (*Ans:* 80 gm-wt; 53.3 gm-wt)

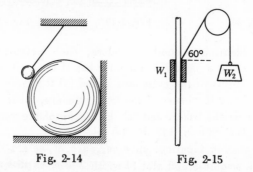

Fig. 2-14   Fig. 2-15

2-28. A block of weight W_1 may move vertically on a frictionless pole. It is supported by a string at 60.0° to the horizontal, passing over a frictionless pulley and attached to a block of weight W_2. If $W_1 = 10.5$ lb, what must be the weight W_2 if the blocks are to remain motionless, as in Fig. 2-15?

2-29. Three blocks of weight W_1, W_2, and W are suspended by flexible, weightless cords and are at rest, as shown in Fig. 2-16. The pul-

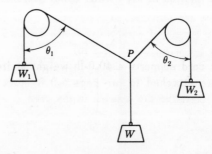

Fig. 2-16

leys are frictionless. (a) Draw in the diagram all forces acting on the point P. (b) Show that

$$W_1 = W \frac{\sin \theta_2}{\sin (\theta_1 + \theta_2)} \quad \text{and} \quad W_2 = W \frac{\sin \theta_1}{\sin (\theta_1 + \theta_2)}.$$

(c) Calculate W_1 and W_2 with $\theta_1 = 60°$, $\theta_2 = 30°$, and $W = 100$ lb. (*Ans:* 50 lb, 87 lb)

2-30. A body of mass 5.0 kg is supported by cords as shown in Fig. 2-17. Calculate the tension in each of the three sections of the cord. (a) Solve graphically. (b) Solve analytically.

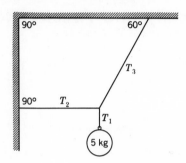

Fig. 2-17

2-31. An acrobat whose weight is 150 lb stands at the middle of a wire which is stretched between two hooks 20.0 ft apart. What is the tension in the wire if the lowest point on the wire is 4.0 in. below the support? (*Ans:* 2250 lb)

2-32. The rope supporting a child's swing is 13.0 ft long. At the moment that the swing is 5.0 ft from the vertical line through the bar supporting it, the tension in the rope is 120 lb. (a) Resolve the tension into horizontal and vertical components. (b) What is the combined weight of child and swing?

2-33. A 20.0-lb picture is supported by a wire from a single hook. The ends of the wire are attached to the picture frame by two screw eyes 24.0 in. apart. The length of wire between the hooks is 26.0 in. Determine the tension in the wire. (*Ans:* 11.3 lb)

2-34. A 10.0-ft cord supports a 40.0-lb weight at its mid-point. The ends of the cord are attached to two pegs 6.0 ft apart and on the same horizontal level. Determine the tension in the cord.

CHAPTER 3

Velocity and Acceleration

Speed is distance per unit time:

$$\text{average speed } \bar{v} = \frac{s}{t},$$

(3-1)

$$\text{instantaneous speed } v = \lim_{\Delta t \to 0} \frac{\Delta s}{\Delta t} = \frac{ds}{dt}.$$

A statement of *velocity* must specify the direction as well as the speed. Examples: 20 mi/hr, east; 16 ft/sec, up.

Acceleration is the time rate of change of velocity:

$$\bar{a} = \frac{v_2 - v_1}{t} \quad \text{or} \quad a = \frac{dv}{dt}.$$

(3-2)

Acceleration is a vector quantity. Examples: 32 ft/sec, down; 3 mi hr^{-1} sec^{-1}, west.

Example: An automobile increases its speed from 20 mi/hr to 50 mi/hr in 10 sec while traveling east. What is the acceleration?

The acceleration, or rate of change of velocity, is the change in eastward speed divided by the time in which it occurred, or

$$\bar{a} = \frac{(50 - 20) \text{ mi } hr^{-1}}{10 \text{ sec}} = \frac{30 \text{ mi/hr}}{10 \text{ sec}} = 3.0 \text{ (mi/hr) per second, east,}$$

indicating that the speed increases 3.0 mi/hr during each second.
Since

$$30 \text{ mi/hr} = \frac{30 \text{ mi/hr} \times 5280 \text{ ft/min}}{3600 \text{ sec/hr}} = 44 \text{ ft/sec,}$$

the acceleration can be written also as

$$\bar{a} = \frac{44 \text{ ft/sec}}{10 \text{ sec}} = 4.4 \text{ ft/sec}^2, \text{ east.}$$

This simply means that the eastward speed increases 4.4 ft/sec during each second, or 4.4 ft/sec².

The equations of *uniformly accelerated motion*, for the particular case in which the direction of motion remains fixed and the speed changes uniformly are

$$s = \bar{v}t, \quad \text{or} \quad s = \int v \, dt, \qquad (3\text{-}3)$$

$$v_2 - v_1 = at, \qquad (3\text{-}4)$$

$$\bar{v} = \frac{v_1 - v_2}{2}, \qquad (3\text{-}5)$$

$$s = v_1 t + \tfrac{1}{2} at^2, \qquad (3\text{-}6)$$

$$2as = v_2^2 - v_1^2. \qquad (3\text{-}7)$$

Example: A train traveling with a speed of 60 mi/hr is brought to rest in 2400 ft. What is the acceleration? What time is required to stop the train?

$$v_1 = 60 \text{ mi/hr} = 88 \text{ ft/sec}, \qquad v_2 = 0.$$

From Eq. (3-7),

$$2as = v_2^2 - v_1^2,$$

$$2a \,(2400 \text{ ft}) = 0 - (88 \text{ ft/sec})^2,$$

$$a = \frac{-(88 \text{ ft/sec})^2}{2\,(2400 \text{ ft})} = -1.8 \text{ ft/sec}^2.$$

From Eq. (3-4),

$$t = \frac{v_2 - v_1}{a} = \frac{0 - 88 \text{ ft/sec}}{-1.8 \text{ ft/sec}^2} = 48 \text{ sec.}$$

Example: A car starts from rest and attains a speed of 30 mi/hr, west, in 18 sec. How far does it travel in this time?

We first find the acceleration:

$$v_1 = 0, \quad v_2 = 30 \text{ mi/hr} = 44 \text{ ft/sec}, \quad t = 18 \text{ sec.}$$

From Eq. (3-4),

$$\bar{a} = \frac{v_2 - v_1}{t} = \frac{44 \text{ ft/sec} - 0}{18 \text{ sec}} = 2.4 \text{ ft/sec}^2 \text{ (west)}.$$

From Eq. (3-6),

$$s = v_1 t + \tfrac{1}{2} at^2 = 0 + \tfrac{1}{2} (2.4 \text{ ft/sec}^2)(18 \text{ sec})^2 = 3\overline{9}0 \text{ ft.}$$

A *freely falling body* is one that is acted upon by no forces of appreciable magnitude other than its weight.

The *acceleration* of a freely falling body (acceleration due to gravity) at sea level and 45° latitude is 32.17 ft/sec² or 980.6 cm/sec².

The *terminal speed* of a falling object is the vertical speed at which the force of air resistance just balances the weight of the object.

Example: A pebble starting from rest falls freely. How far does it fall during the first second? What is its speed at the end of 1.0 sec?

$$v_1 = 0, \quad a = 32 \text{ ft/sec}^2 \text{ (down)}, \quad t = 1.0 \text{ sec.}$$

From Eq. (3-6),

$$s = v_1 t + \tfrac{1}{2} at^2 = 0 + \tfrac{1}{2} (32 \text{ ft/sec}^2)(1.0 \text{ sec})^2 = 16 \text{ ft.}$$

From Eq. (3-4),

$$v_2 = v_1 + at = 0 + (32 \text{ ft/sec}^2)(1.0 \text{ sec}) = 32 \text{ ft/sec (down)}.$$

Example: A ball is thrown upward with an initial speed of 52 ft/sec. Find (a) the distance traveled during the first second, (b) the speed at the end of the first second, (c) the highest elevation reached by the ball, and (d) the total time of flight.

(a) $v_1 = 52 \text{ ft/sec (up)}, \quad a = -32 \text{ ft/sec}^2, \quad t = 1.0 \text{ sec.}$

From Eq. (3-6),

$$s = v_1 t + \tfrac{1}{2} at^2$$

$$= (52 \text{ ft/sec})(1.0 \text{ sec}) + \tfrac{1}{2}(-32 \text{ ft/sec}^2)(1.0 \text{ sec})^2 = 36 \text{ ft.}$$

(b) From Eq. (3-4),

$$v_2 = v_1 + at$$

$$= 52 \text{ ft/sec} + (-32 \text{ ft/sec}^2)(1.0 \text{ sec}) = 20 \text{ ft/sec.}$$

(c) At the highest point, the ball stops, and hence $v_2 = 0$.
From Eq. (3-7),

$$2as = v_2^2 - v_1^2,$$

$$2(-32 \text{ ft/sec}^2)(s) = 0 - (52 \text{ ft/sec})^2,$$

$$s = \frac{-(52 \text{ ft/sec})^2}{2\,(-32 \text{ ft/sec}^2)} = 42 \text{ ft.}$$

(d) The time of upward flight is

$$t = \frac{s}{v} = \frac{42 \text{ ft}}{\frac{1}{2}(50 + 0) \text{ ft/sec}} = 1.6 \text{ sec.}$$

An equal time will be required for the ball to return. Hence the total time of flight is 3.2 sec.

Example: A man jumps from a plane, delays opening his parachute, and reaches a terminal speed of 120 mi/hr, downward. When he opens his 'chute, his terminal speed becomes 14 mi/hr in 4.0 sec. (a) What acceleration does he experience in this interval? (b) From what height on a ladder would a man have to jump to have the same vertical landing speed?

(a) $\quad \overline{a} = \dfrac{v_2 - v_1}{t} = \dfrac{14 \text{ mi/hr} - 120 \text{ mi/hr}}{4.0 \text{ sec}}$

$$= -26 \frac{\text{mi/hr}}{\text{sec}} = -39 \text{ ft/sec}^2.$$

(b) Landing speed = 14 mi/hr = 21 ft/sec. To acquire this speed in free fall would require a distance s:

$$s = \frac{v_2^2 - v_1^2}{2\,a} = \frac{(21 \text{ ft/sec})^2 - 0}{2\,(32 \text{ ft/sec}^2)} = 6.9 \text{ ft.}$$

Example: A ball dropped from the roof of a tall building passes a window ledge with a speed of 96 ft/sec and 1.0 sec later strikes the ground. (a) What is the height of the window? (b) How tall is the building?

(a) $\quad s = v_1 t + \frac{1}{2} a t^2$

$$= (96 \text{ ft/sec})\,(1.0 \text{ sec}) + \frac{1}{2}\,(32 \text{ ft/sec}^2)\,(1.0 \text{ sec})^2 = 1\overline{1}0 \text{ ft.}$$

(b) The maximum speed is

$$v_2 = 2\,as = 2\,(32 \text{ ft/sec}^2)\,(112 \text{ ft}) = 128 \text{ ft/sec.}$$

Height of roof above ledge is

$$s' = \frac{v_1^2}{2\,a} = \frac{(96 \text{ ft/sec})^2}{2\,(32 \text{ ft/sec}^2)} = 1\overline{4}0 \text{ ft.}$$

Total height of building equals

$$112 \text{ ft} + 140 \text{ ft} = 2\overline{6}0 \text{ ft.}$$

Curvilinear motion in a plane may be represented by a path like that in Fig. 3-1. The average velocity between points 1 and 2 is defined as

$$\bar{v} = \frac{\mathbf{r}_2 - \mathbf{r}_1}{t_2 - t_1},$$

where the numerator is a vector difference of the displacements $\mathbf{r}_2$ and $\mathbf{r}_1$. The instantaneous velocity of a particle moving on a curve is a vector, tangent to the curve at the point considered, whose magnitude is equal to the speed of the particle along the curve.

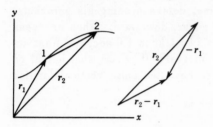

Fig. 3-1(a) Curvilinear motion: velocity.

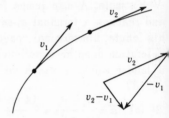

Fig. 3-1(b) Curvilinear motion: acceleration.

The instantaneous acceleration is the limiting value of the expression $(v_2 - v_1)/(t_2 - t_1)$ as t_2 approaches t_1.

In uniform circular motion, a particle travels at a constant speed in a circular path. But since its velocity continually changes its direction, the acceleration vector is not zero. By considering triangles in Fig. 3-2,

$$\Delta v = \frac{cv}{r}, \qquad \text{magnitude of } a = \lim_{t_2 \to t_1} \frac{v}{t_2 - t_1}.$$

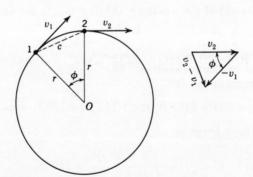

Fig. 3-2. Acceleration in uniform circular motion.

In the limit,

$$c \to s = v(t_2 - t_1),$$

therefore,

$$a = \lim_{t_2 \to t_1} \frac{v^2(t_2 - t_1)}{\mathbf{r}(t_2 - t_1)}, \qquad a = \frac{v^2}{\mathbf{r}}.$$

A particle in uniform circular motion has an acceleration of magnitude $v^2/\mathbf{r}$ which is always directed toward the center of the circle.

PROBLEMS

Velocity, acceleration

3-1. An airplane makes a take-off run of 810 ft; it leaves the ground after 18.0 sec. (a) What was its acceleration (assumed constant) during the run? (b) With what speed does it take off? (*Ans:* 1.25 ft/sec²; 153 mi/hr)

3-2. Starting from rest, a car is able to reach a speed of 60 mi/hr in 20 sec. Calculate (a) the average acceleration, and (b) the distance traveled in reaching 60 mi/hr.

3-3. A body is deflected through an angle of 30° with no change in speed. What was the direction of its average acceleration? (Give the angle in degrees between acceleration and initial velocity.) (*Ans:* 105°)

3-4. Rain is falling so as to make streaks on the side windows of a train that has an acceleration of 88 ft sec⁻¹ min⁻¹. If the angle that the streaks make with the horizontal changes from 45° to 11° 20′ in 1 min, what is the velocity of the falling rain if it is assumed to fall vertically? (*Ans:* 22 ft/sec)

3-5. A body moves such that its distance x, in feet, from a point A is expressed by the relation $x = 5t^2 - 3t + 6$, in which t is expressed in seconds. (a) What is its speed when $t = 2.0$ sec? (b) What is the acceleration? (c) How far is the body from A at the end of 10 sec? (*Ans:* 17 ft/sec; 10 ft/sec²; 476 ft)

3-6. A wheel of radius 2.0 ft rolls such that the velocity of the center is 6.0 ft/sec, in the x-direction. What are the velocities and accelerations of points A and B in Fig. 3-3?

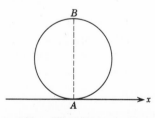

Fig. 3-3

Free fall

3-7. A ball is thrown vertically upward from the top of a tower with an initial speed of 80 ft/sec. What is the position of the ball relative to the top of the tower after 6.0 sec? (*Ans:* 95 ft below top)

3-8. An arrow is shot vertically upward with a speed of 128 ft/sec. Neglecting air resistance, how high does it rise?

3-9. With what velocity must a steel ball be thrown straight up to attain a height of 4410 cm? (*Ans:* 2940 cm/sec)

3-10. A balloon rises from the earth with a constant speed of 10.0 ft/sec. A stone dropped from the balloon reaches the ground in 3.0 sec. Find (a) the height of the balloon at the instant the stone was dropped, (b) the height of the balloon when the stone reaches the ground, and (c) the speed of the stone as it reaches the ground.

3-11. A man is working in a basket attached to a balloon which is rising at a uniform rate of 32 ft/sec with respect to the ground, when he accidentally drops overboard a hammer which weighs 0.279 lb. The hammer strikes the earth 10.0 sec later. (a) What is the velocity of the hammer with respect to the ground at the instant it is dropped? (b) How high is the balloon at the instant the hammer is dropped? (*Ans:* 32 ft/sec, downward; 1280 ft)

3-12. A pebble is dropped in a well and by stopwatch it is found that 4.25 sec elapse after release of the pebble before the splash is heard. If the speed of sound in the well is 313.6 m/sec, what is the depth to the water surface? (*Ans:* 78.2 m)

3-13. A brick is thrown practically straight up with an initial speed of 80 ft/sec. It lands on the edge of a roof 64 ft above its starting point. (a) How high does it rise? (b) How much time is spent on the way up? (c) With what velocity does it land? (d) For how long a time is it in motion? (*Ans:* 100 ft; 2.5 sec; 48 ft/sec; 4.0 sec)

3-14. A stone is thrown vertically upward with a speed of 72.0 ft/sec from the top of a tower 62.0 ft high. (a) When will the stone reach its maximum height? (b) When will it pass a point 30.0 ft above the tower? (c) When will the stone reach the ground?

Uniform circular motion

3-15. A 20-gm weight makes 2.00 rev/sec on the end of a 10.0 cm string. What is its centripetal acceleration? (*Ans:* 1580 cm/sec²)

3-16. A point moves over a circular path 10 cm in diameter 4 times per second. How great is its acceleration?

Uniformly accelerated motion

3-17. An automobile accelerates from rest at a constant rate and passes two points 80.0 ft apart in 2.0 sec. Its speed as it passes the second point is 50.0 ft/sec. Find (a) its acceleration, (b) the distance of the second point from the start. (*Ans:* 5.0 ft/sec², 250 ft)

3-18. Who would win a 100-yd dash, a runner who can cover the distance in 10.0 sec or an automobile which can accelerate to 60 mi/hr from rest in 16 sec? By how much?

3-19. An automobile and a truck start from rest at the same instant, with the automobile initially at some distance behind the truck. The truck and automobile have constant accelerations of 4.0 and 6.0 ft/sec², respectively, and the automobile overtakes the truck after the truck has moved 150 ft. (a) How long does it take the auto to overtake the truck? (b) How far was the auto behind the truck initially? (c) What is the speed of each when they are abreast? (*Ans:* 8.7 sec; 75 ft; 35 ft/sec).

3-20. A train starting from rest travels 240 mi with uniform acceleration, attaining a final speed of 60 mi/hr. For the next two hours the train travels at a uniform speed of 60 mi/hr. (a) How long does the train take to travel the first 240 mi? (b) What is the acceleration of the train in the first 240 mi? (c) What is the average speed for the entire trip?

3-21. The brakes are suddenly applied in a car with an initial speed of 60 mi/hr, slowing it down to 30 mi/hr in a time of 4.0 sec. Find (a) the acceleration, (b) the distance traveled during those 4.0 sec, and (c) the speed at the end of 3.0 sec. (*Ans:* 7.5 mi/hr per sec, 180 ft, 37 mi/hr)

3-22. An automobile starts at the rear of a column of marching soldiers, travels to the front of the column, turns around and returns to the rear of the column. If the speed of the automobile is 25 mi/hr and the trip takes 30 min, (a) how long is the column, and (b) how far did the automobile travel?

3-23. A rock thrown in a vertical direction from the edge of a 500-ft cliff struck the floor of the valley 6.00 sec later. What was the initial speed of the rock? Was it up or down? (*Ans:* 12.6 ft/sec, upward)

3-24. A rocket used for upper atmosphere research is accelerated upward by its motor for only a short time; the rocket then decelerates under the force of gravity, "coasting" up to a very high altitude. Suppose that the motors of a rocket that starts from the ground are "on" for only 10.0 sec and that at the end of this time the rocket has attained an upward velocity of 1 mi/sec (take this to be 5000 ft/sec). Assuming that the acceleration due to the thrust of the rocket is uniform and neglecting air resistance (for such speed this is really a poor approximation), calculate (a) the height at which the rocket motors cease, (b) the maximum altitude (in miles) which the rocket attains, (c) the total time spent in flight.

3-25. The locomotive of a freight train passes a station moving at 4.0 mi/hr and accelerating at a constant rate. One minute later the caboose passes the station going 16 mi/hr. (a) What is the acceleration? (b) How long is the train? (*Ans:* 0.29 ft/sec²; 0.17 mi)

3-26. A truck goes through a red light and continues to travel at 30 mi/hr. At the instant the truck passes it at the intersection a waiting car assumes that the light has changed and starts up in the same direction as the truck with a constant acceleration of 12 ft/sec². Two seconds later a motorcycle officer leaves the intersection with a constant acceleration. If he wishes to catch both offenders, what should be the value of his acceleration to reach the car just as it is passing the truck? (*Ans:* 23 ft/sec²)

3-27. A fast train running at a speed v_1 rounds a hill onto a straightaway; the engineer observes at a distance d a slower train on the same track going in the same direction with a speed v_2. The engineer instantly applies his brakes, which give a constant deceleration of $-a$ to the faster train. Determine the formula for the minimum value of d such that there shall be no rear-end collision. *Ans:* $d \geq \dfrac{(v_1 - v_2)^2}{2a}$

3-28. A destroyer is proceeding through a fog on a course N 45° E. The fog lifts for a moment, and the destroyer observes, due east, an enemy cruiser proceeding on a north course at a range of 5.0 mi. The cruiser does not observe the destroyer, and both vessels continue on their courses. One and one-half minutes later the fog again lifts for a moment, and this time the enemy cruiser is observed to be due east of the destroyer at a range of 4.0 mi. The fog closes in and again both vessels continue on their courses. Ten seconds after the second ragging, the destroyer fires a shell with a muzzle velocity of 1600 ft/sec. If the shell is to hit the cruiser, at what compass angle must it be fired? (*Ans:* Due east)

3-29. A bomber making a run against an anti-aircraft gun releases a bomb and continues on its horizontal course. Twenty seconds after the bomb release, the antiaircraft gun fires a shell with a 5-sec fuse straight upward. Both gun and bomber score perfect hits at the same instant. (a) How high was the bomber flying? (b) What was the muzzle velocity of the shell? (*Ans:* 10⁴ ft; 2080 ft/sec)

3-30. A submarine ups periscope and observes, 2000 yd due east, an enemy destroyer traveling at 35 mi/hr on a course due north. The submarine carries torpedoes that travel 40 mi/hr in the water and sink after going 5.0 mi. If, without moving from its position, it takes the submarine 1.0 min to turn, aim, and fire a torpedo, (a) will it waste a torpedo if it fires one? (b) What is the maximum time the submarine can take in aiming and firing at the destroyer without wasting a torpedo? (*Ans:* Yes; 50 sec)

Projectile motion

3-31. A projectile is fired with a speed of 300 ft/sec at an angle of 37° with the horizontal. Compute the speed when it first reaches a height of 400 ft. (*Ans:* 83.5 ft/sec)

3-32. A mortar shell is projected upward with a speed of 200 ft/sec at an angle of 45° with the horizontal. (a) What is its initial vertical velocity? (b) What is its vertical velocity after 2.0 sec? (c) What is its horizontal velocity after 2.0 sec? (d) When the shell is descending, it strikes a building at a point 64 ft above the ground. What is the vertical component of the velocity at the instant the shell strikes? (*Ans:* $1\overline{4}0$ ft/sec; 77 ft/sec; $1\overline{4}0$ ft/sec; 32 ft/sec)

3-33. A baseball player throws a baseball in from the outfield. As it leaves the player's hand, the ball makes an angle of 60° with the horizontal. After 2.0 sec the ball is still rising, but in a direction 30° above the horizontal. Compute the speed of the ball when released by the player. Neglect air friction. (*Ans:* $1\overline{1}0$ ft/sec)

3-34. A gun is aimed at an angle of 30° above a level plain. The shell rises 600 ft above the plain. (a) How far will the shell travel horizontally? (b) What is its velocity in magnitude and direction after 4.0 sec of flight?

3-35. A ball is thrown at an angle of 60° with the horizontal with a velocity of $320/\sqrt{3}$ (ft/sec). (a) How high will it rise? (b) What is the range? (c) Where will the ball be at the end of 6 sec? (*Ans:* $4\overline{0}0$ ft; $9\overline{3}0$ ft; $x = 5\overline{6}0$ ft, $y = 3\overline{8}0$ ft)

3-36. A baseball rolls down a roof which makes an angle of 37° with the horizontal. When the ball reaches the lower edge of the roof its speed is 30 ft/sec. If this edge of the roof is 20 ft above level ground, at what horizontal distance from the edge will the ball strike the ground?

3-37. A batted baseball leaves the bat at an angle of 37° with the horizontal and with a velocity of 120 ft/sec. The ball is caught by a spectator in the outfield bleachers at a horizontal distance of 384 ft from home plate. How far above the level at which the ball was struck was it caught? (*Ans:* 33 ft)

3-38. A stone is thrown from a 480-ft cliff, overhanging a lake, with a velocity which has a vertical component of 16 ft/sec, upward. (a) How high will the stone rise before its upward speed is reduced to zero? (b) How many seconds will elapse before it strikes the water?

3-39. A golf ball is driven from a tee with a velocity of 200 ft/sec at an angle of 37° above the horizontal. It strikes a green at a horizontal distance of 1280 ft from the tee. Was the green above or below the tee, and by how much? (*Ans:* 4 ft below)

3-40. A punted football traveled 64 yd along the ground and stayed in the air 6.0 sec. (a) How high did it rise? (b) What was the vertical component of the ball's initial velocity? (c) What was the horizontal component of the ball's initial velocity? (d) With what velocity did the ball leave the kicker's foot?

CHAPTER 4

Force and Motion

The relation between forces and the motions produced by them was described by Newton in three laws of motion. They are:

1. A body at rest remains at rest and a body in motion continues to move at constant speed in a straight line unless acted upon by an external, unbalanced force.
2. An unbalanced force acting on a body produces an acceleration in the direction of the net force. This acceleration is proportional to the force and inversely proportional to the mass of the body.
3. For every acting force, there is a reacting force equal in magnitude but opposite in direction. (Here the term "acting force" means the force that one body exerts on a second body, while "reacting force" means the force that the second body exerts on the first.)

The relation expressed in Newton's second law may be written in equation form as

$$F = kma, \tag{4-1}$$

where F, m, and a can be in any units, provided the proper value is assigned to k, or

$$F = ma, \tag{4-2}$$

where one can use *only* those consistent sets of units which (by definition of one of the units) make $k = 1$. One such consistent set is: F in newtons, m in kilograms, and a in meters per second per second. Other sets of consistent units are shown in Table 4-1.

The *newton* is defined as the force that will impart to a 1-kg mass an acceleration of 1 m/sec^2.

The *dyne* is defined as the force that will impart to a 1-gm mass an acceleration of 1 cm/sec^2.

The *poundal* is defined as the force that will impart to a 1-lb mass an acceleration of 1 ft/sec^2.

The *slug* is the mass to which a force of 1 lb will give an acceleration of 1 ft/sec^2.

The *mass m* of a body is the numerical measure of its inertia, in terms of an arbitrary standard mass; for example, the standard kilogram.

The *weight W* of a body is the force with which the body is pulled vertically downward by the attraction of the earth (the force of gravity).

Table 4-1. Consistent Systems of Units for Newton's Second Law

System	Unit of mass	Unit of force	Unit of acceleration
mks (absolute)	kilogram	newton*	meter/second^2
cgs absolute..........	gram	dyne*	centimeter/second^2
cgs gravitational ..	No name assigned $m = W/g$	gram	centimeter/second^2
British absolute....	pound	poundal*	foot/second^2
British gravitational......	slug*	pound	foot/second^2
Any system............	W/g	Same units as that used for W	Same unit as that used for g

*In each set, the starred unit is the one usually defined from the second law so as to make $k = 1$ in $F = kma$.

When a body falls freely, the net force acting on it (its weight W) produces the acceleration g. If another net force F is applied to the same body, a different acceleration, a, will be produced:

$$\frac{F}{W} = \frac{a}{g}$$

(4-3)

or

$$F = \frac{W}{g}\, a.$$

In this equation any units can be used provided the force F and weight W are in the same units of force and a and g are in the same units of acceleration.

The law of universal gravitation expresses the fact that every particle attracts every other particle with a force directly proportional to the product of their masses and inversely proportional to the square of the distance between them:

$$F = G\,\frac{m_1 m_2}{s^2}.$$

(4-4)

The value of the gravitational constant G is 6.670×10^{-11} newton-m^2/kg^2.

Example: A net force of 1.50 newtons is applied to an object with a mass of 0.75 kg. What acceleration is produced?

$$F = ma,$$

$$a = \frac{F}{a} = \frac{1.50 \text{ newton}}{0.75 \text{ kg}}$$

$$= \frac{1.50 \text{ kg-m/sec}^2}{0.75 \text{ kg}} = 2.0 \text{ m/sec}^2.$$

(*Note*: From Eq. (4-2), 1 newton = 1 kg-m/sec².)

Example: A net force of 3.0 lb acts on a block that weighs 15 lb. What acceleration is produced? From Eq. (4-3),

$$a = \frac{g}{W} F$$

$$= \frac{32 \text{ ft/sec}^2 \times 3.0 \text{ lb}}{15 \text{ lb}} = 6.4 \text{ ft/sec}^2.$$

Example: A 1-lb body collides with a second body of unknown mass. At a certain instant the magnitude of the acceleration of the 1-lb body is 12 ft/sec² and that of the second body is 4 ft/sec². What is the mass of the second body?

From Newton's third law,

$$F_1 = F_2.$$

From Newton's second law,

$$m_1 a_1 = m_2 a_2,$$

$$m_2 = \frac{a_1}{a_2} m_1 = \frac{12 \text{ ft/sec}^2}{4.0 \text{ ft/sec}^2} 1.0 \text{ lb} = 3.0 \text{ lb (mass)}.$$

Example: Two 2-lb cylinders are suspended by a light string over a frictionless pulley of negligible mass. A 0.3-lb disk is then added to one side. (a) What is the resulting acceleration of the system? (b) How far down will the loaded cylinder move in 2 sec after release? (c) What is the tension in the string?

Suggestions: (1) Make a sketch showing the conditions of the problem. Indicate on it dimensions or other data given in the problem.

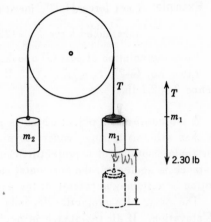

Fig. 4-1. Atwood machine. A problem requiring application of the equations of motion to two bodies.

(2) Select for consideration the one body whose motion is to be studied. Construct a force vector diagram, representing by vectors acting at a point all the forces acting on the body that has been selected. If any forces are unknown, represent them also as vectors and label them unknown quantities.

(3) From the vector diagram, find the resultant force acting on the body. This is the F of Eq. (4-2).

In this problem,

$$\text{total mass} = \frac{2.00 + 2.30}{32.16} \text{ slug} = 0.134 \text{ slug},$$

$$\text{unbalanced force} = 0.30 \text{ lb}.$$

(4) Find the unknown acceleration from the relation $F = ma$. If the weight of the body is given, compute m from $m = W/g$. If the problem is to find a distance, velocity, or time, apply the equations of uniformly accelerated motion, Eqs. (3-3) to (3-7), as required.

From Eq. (4-2),

$$a = \frac{F}{m} = \frac{0.30 \text{ lb}}{0.134 \text{ slug}} = 2.\overline{2}4 \text{ ft/sec}^2.$$

From Eq. (3-6),

$$s = \tfrac{1}{2} a t^2 = \tfrac{1}{2} (2.24 \text{ ft/sec}^2)(2.0 \text{ sec})^2 = 4.5 \text{ ft}.$$

To find the tension T in the string, consider the forces acting on the right-hand load:

$$\text{mass } m_1 = \frac{2.30}{32.16} \text{ slug} = 0.0716 \text{ slug},$$

force upward $= T$, force downward $= 2.30$ lb,

unbalanced force $F_1 = (2.3 \text{ lb} - T)$ downward.

From the solution of part (a) above, $a = 2.24 \text{ ft/sec}^2$.

From Eq. (4-2), $F_1 = m_1 a = (2.3 \text{ lb} - T) = 0.0716 \text{ slug} \times 2.\overline{24} \text{ ft/sec}^2$. Hence $T = 2.1$ lb.

A *projectile* is an object which is given an initial velocity and which is then allowed to move under the action of gravity. The vertical and horizontal motions of a projectile can be treated separately. If air resistance is neglected, the horizontal motion is uniform, while the vertical motion is uniformly accelerated; the path is a parabola.

The *range* of a projectile depends on its initial speed and the angle of elevation. If air resistance is negligible, maximum range is attained with an angle of $45°$. Air resistance decreases the speed, the maximum height, and the range of a projectile.

The motion of *self-propelled* projectiles is not determined by an initial impulse only, but depends on fuel carried within the projectile for a continuing thrust. The initial speeds of self-propelled projectiles are usually small, but they may reach much higher final speeds than ordinary projectiles.

Example: A projectile is thrown with a speed of 120 ft/sec directed $30°$ above the horizontal. Find the height attained, the time of flight, t', and the horizontal range R.

Horizontal velocity $v_h = v \cos \theta = 120 \text{ ft/sec} (\cos 30°) = 104 \text{ ft/sec}$.

Vertical velocity $v_v = v \sin \theta = 120 \text{ ft/sec} (\sin 30°) = 60 \text{ ft/sec}$.

For the vertical motion Eq. (3-7) gives: $v_2^2 - v_1^2 = 2as$, $v_1 = 60 \text{ ft/sec}$, $v_2 = 0$,

$$a = -32 \text{ ft/sec}^2,$$

$$0 - (60 \text{ ft/sec})^2 = (-32 \text{ ft/sec}^2) s,$$

$$s = \frac{3600 \text{ ft}^2/\text{sec}^2}{60 \text{ ft/sec}^2} = 56.3 \text{ ft, the height attained.}$$

The time t to reach the highest point is obtained from:

$$v_2 - v_1 = at.$$

$$0 - 60 \text{ ft/sec} = (-32 \text{ ft/sec}^2) t,$$

$$t = \frac{60 \text{ ft/sec}}{32 \text{ ft/sec}^2} = 1.87 \text{ sec.}$$

The total time t' of flight is:

$$t' = 2t = 2(1.87 \text{ sec}) = 3.74 \text{ sec.}$$

The projectile travels horizontally with uniform speed 104 ft/sec for 3.74 sec. The horizontal range is therefore

$$R = v_h t' = (104 \text{ ft/sec})(3.74 \text{ sec}) = 396 \text{ ft.}$$

PROBLEMS

Newton's second law

4-1. A force of 4900 dynes acts on a 20-gm mass for 8.0 sec. (a) What acceleration is caused? (b) How far does the mass move from rest in the 8.0 sec? (c) How fast is it going at the end of 8.0 sec? (*Ans:* $2\overline{4}5$ cm/sec²; $8\overline{1}40$ cm; $1\overline{9}60$ cm/sec)

4-2. Distinguish between action-at-a-distance forces and contact forces. Give two examples of each.

4-3. A 16-lb block has a rope attached to it which has a maximum tensile strength of 25 lb. What is the least time in which the block can be raised vertically through a distance of 36 ft by pulling on the rope? (*Ans:* 1.2 sec)

4-4. A 10-lb hammer moving with a speed of 18 ft/sec strikes a nail and drives it 0.50 in. into a block of wood. Assume that the hammer is decelerated at a constant rate. Compute (a) the time required for the hammer to stop after it comes into contact with the nail, (b) the force exerted on the nail.

4-5. A girl pushes her baby brother in a 40-lb carriage. In order to move at a constant velocity of 2.0 ft/sec along a level sidewalk she pushes with a force of 5.0 lb. The carriage comes to a patch of ice on the sidewalk (no friction) and the girl continues to push for 1.2 sec before she realizes she is going too fast, viz., 5.0 ft/sec. What is the weight of the baby? (*Ans:* 24 lb)

4-6. The string of a bow is 5.0 ft long. When an archer draws the bow, it is bent so that the ends of the string are 4.0 ft apart. The archer's pull on the string is 30 lb. (a) Assuming that the string has not stretched, what is the tension in the string? (b) If, as the bow is released, the average force acting on the arrow is 15 lb, the force acts for a time t during which the arrow is accelerated to a velocity of 320 ft/sec, and the weight of the arrow is 0.10 lb, what is the time t? (c) Two seconds after leaving the bow, the arrow hits a target at the same elevation. How high did the arrow rise in its flight?

4-7. A train traveling at 50 mi/hr is brought uniformly to a stop in 22.8 sec. During this acceleration, (a) at what angle with the vertical does a plumb bob hang in one of the coaches, and (b) if the tender is half full of water, and is 11 times as long as it is deep, will water spill over, and if so, from which end? (*Ans:* 5°43′; Yes, forward end)

4-8. Two trains leave a station simultaneously, moving in the same direction on parallel tracks. Train A is accelerated at 15 mi/hr per min and train B at 5 mi/hr per min. At the end of 3.0 min, (a) what is the speed of each? (b) How far has each moved? (c) What is the speed of A relative to B?

4-9. If each of the locomotives of the trains in problem 4-8 exerted the same drawbar pull, (a) what is the ratio of the mass of train A to that of train B? (b) If both locomotives were connected to train A, what acceleration could be achieved? Neglect friction. (*Ans:* ⅓, 30 mi/hr per min)

4-10. The normal motorist has a "reaction time" of 0.7 sec. Assume that, by means of the brakes, a retarding force equal to 2/3 of the weight of the car can be applied to the car. If a 2800-lb car is traveling at 45 mi/hr, find (a) the acceleration when the brakes are applied, and (b) the distance in which the car can be stopped. (c) How does this distance compare with the distance in which a heavier car would be stopped?

Inclined plane

4-11. An incline rises 5.0 ft in each 13.0 ft of the incline. To push a 100-lb body up the incline at uniform speed a force of 57 lb parallel to the incline is necessary. What force, parallel to the incline, is necessary to push the body down the incline at a uniform speed? (*Ans:* 20 lb)

4-12. Find the acceleration of the two blocks in Fig. 4-2, where $m_1 = 64$ lb, $m_2 = 96$ lb, and $\theta = 30°$. What is the tension in the rope?

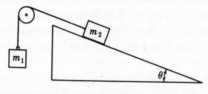

Fig. 4-2

4-13. Block A (4.0 lb) rests on a smooth board inclined at 30° with respect to a level table top. A cord passes from A over a frictionless pulley to an 8.0 lb block B hanging at the side of the table. Find the acceleration of the blocks when released. (*Ans:* 16 ft/sec²)

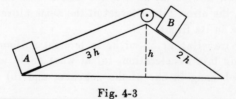

Fig. 4-3

4-14. Two identical blocks of mass m are connected by a string $3h$ long on a double plane with dimensions as shown in Fig. 4-3. How fast will block A be moving when block B hits the ground? The surfaces are frictionless. (Ans: $\sqrt{gh/3}$)

4-15. In the system pictured in Fig. 4-4, a block weighing 34 kg slides along a smooth plane of height 7.0 m and length 15 m. The ball suspended at the high end of the plane has a mass of 9.0 kg; the ball at the low end has a mass of 29 kg. The system is released when the lower ball is 3.5 m above ground. How fast is the lower ball moving when it reaches the ground? (Ans: 720 cm sec)

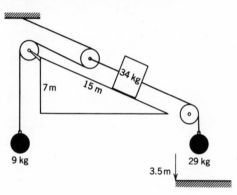

Fig. 4-4

Horizontal, frictionless surface

4-16. A 30-lb block resting on a smooth table is tied to a cord running over a light frictionless pulley to an 18-lb block at the lower end of the cord. Find (a) the accelerations of the two masses, and (b) the tension in the cord. (c) Make a diagram showing all forces acting on the masses.

4-17. In the arrangement shown in Fig. 4-5, $m_1 = 100$ gm, $m_2 = 400$ gm, $m_3 = 200$ gm, the pulleys are massless, and the surfaces are frictionless. What is the acceleration of m_2? (Ans: $0.2g$)

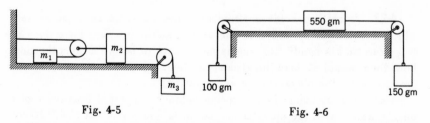

Fig. 4-5   Fig. 4-6

4-18. Find the tensions in the two strings in Fig. 4-6, assuming no friction.

4-19. Find the acceleration of the masses and the tensions in the rope for the arrangement shown in Fig. 4-7. The rope ends are tied at point P. (Ans: 490 cm/sec^2, 4.9 × 10^5 dynes)

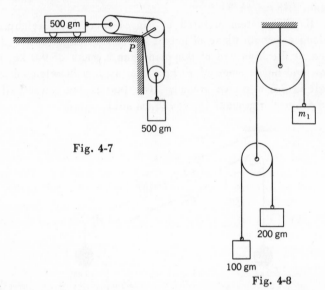

Fig. 4-7

Fig. 4-8

4-20. In the system of Fig. 4-8, (a) What should be the value of m_1 such that the 100-gm mass does not move? (b) If m_1 has this value, what is its acceleration? (Ans: 160 gm; 1/4 g)

Newton's third law

4-21. What is the fallacy in the following argument? "A horse pulls on a cart. By Newton's third law the cart pulls back on the horse with a force equal to that exerted by the horse on the cart. Hence the sum of the forces is zero, from which it follows that it is not possible for the horse to accelerate the cart."

Elevator

4-22. A bellhop holds a 10-kg suitcase while he is in an elevator which accelerates upward at a rate of 2 m/sec^2. (a) What force does the bag exert on his hand? (b) Supposing the bag to be 0.6 m from the floor, how long would it take to strike the floor of the elevator if it were dropped while the elevator were accelerating?

4-23. A body hangs from a spring balance supported from the roof of an elevator. (a) If the elevator has an upward acceleration of 4.0 ft/sec^2 and the balance reads 45 lb, what is the true weight of the body? (b) In what circumstances will the balance read 35 lb? (c) What will the balance read if the elevator cable breaks? (*Ans:* 40 lb; $a = 4.0$ ft/sec^2 downward; zero)

Projectiles (See also Chapter 3.)

4-24. A girl standing on a diving board throws a ball with a horizontal velocity of 50 ft/sec to a man in the water. In doing so, she loses her balance, falls off the board and strikes the water in 2.0 sec. (a) How far is the man from the base of the diving board? (b) How high is the diving board above the water? (c) What is the final velocity of the ball? (*Ans:* 100 ft; 64 ft; 81 ft/sec, at 52° with the horizontal)

Gravitation

4-25. Find the mass of the earth from the following experimental data: $g = 9.80$ m/sec^2 and $G = 6.67 \times 10^{-11}$ newton-m^2/kg. The radius of the earth is 6.37×10^6 m. (*Ans:* 5.98×10^{24} kg = 6.59×10^{21} tons)

4-26. (a) What is meant by the gravitational constant? How may it be measured? (b) If the mass of the moon is 1/80 the mass of the earth and the diameter is 1/4 that of the earth, what is the acceleration of gravity on the moon? (c) How far will a 2.0-gm mass fall in 1.0 sec on the moon? (*Ans:* (b) 1/5 g; (c) 3.2 ft)

4-27. Two equal masses, which may be considered as particles, attract each other with a force of 2.0×10^{-6} dyne when they are 10.0 cm apart. What is the distance between the two masses when the attraction is 3.0×10^{-6} dyne? (*Ans:* 8.2 cm)

Atwood machine

4-28. An Atwood machine consists of two 1000-gm masses hung by a string over a massless, frictionless pulley. To determine "g" a 20.0-gm rider is added to one side and it is found that at the end of 2.00 sec the system has moved 19.2 cm, starting from rest. Find (a) the acceleration of the system, and (b) "g."

4-29. An 11.0-lb and a 9.0-lb block are suspended by a cord passing over a frictionless, massless pulley. (a) What force is available to cause acceleration? (b) How much mass will be accelerated? (c) What is the numerical value of the acceleration? (d) What is the tension in the string? (*Ans:* 2.0 lb; 0.62 slug; 3.2 ft/sec^2; 8.1 lb)

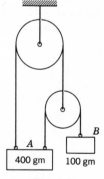

Fig. 4-9

4-30. Find the accelerations of the masses A and B in Fig. 4-9, and the tension in the cords. (*Ans:* 75, 226 cm sec^2; 123, 246 gm)

4-31. Find the accelerations of masses C and D in Fig. 4-10, and the tensions in the cords. (*Ans:* 420, 140 cm/sec^2; 114, 342 gm)

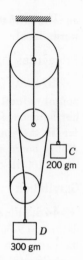

In Chapter 3, it was shown that in *uniform circular motion* the magnitude of the central acceleration is given by

$$a_c = \frac{v^2}{r} = \omega^2 r. \qquad (4\text{-}5)$$

The *centripetal force,* the inward force that causes the central acceleration, is given by

$$F_c = m \frac{v^2}{r}. \qquad (4\text{-}6)$$

Fig. 4-10

A *centrifugal reaction* is exerted by the moving body on the agent of its centripetal force. From Newton's third law, the magnitude of the centrifugal reaction is equal to that of the centripetal force.

The proper *banking* of a curve to eliminate need for a sidewise frictional force is given by the relation

$$\frac{\overline{AB}}{\overline{BC}} = \frac{v^2}{gr} = \tan\theta. \qquad (4\text{-}7)$$

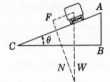

Fig. 4-11. Banking a curve.

Example: A curve on a highway has a radius of 160 ft. If the pavement is 28 ft wide and its outer edge is 3.5 ft higher than the inside edge, for what speed is it ideally banked?

From Eq. (4-7),

$$v = \sqrt{\frac{\overline{AB}}{\overline{BC}}gr} = \sqrt{\frac{(3.5\text{ ft})(32\text{ ft/sec}^2)(160\text{ ft})}{28\text{ ft}}} = 25.3\text{ ft/sec} = 37\text{ mi/hr}.$$

Example: A pilot doing an inside loop nearly falls from his seat at the top of the loop, where the plane is going 90 mi/hr. What is the radius of the loop?

$$m\frac{v^2}{r} = W,$$

$$r = \frac{m}{W}v^2 = \frac{v^2}{g} = \frac{(137\text{ ft/sec})^2}{32\text{ ft/sec}^2} = 5\overline{4}5\text{ ft}.$$

The *momentum* of a body is the product of its mass and its velocity. Momentum is a vector quantity.

$$p = mv. \tag{4-8}$$

The law of *conservation of momentum* states that the momentum of a body or a system of bodies does not change unless an unbalanced external force acts upon it.

Impulse is the product of a force and the time during which it acts. Impulse is equal to the change in momentum.

$$Ft = mv_2 - mv_1. \tag{4-9}$$

The *coefficient of restitution* is the ratio of the relative velocity of separation to the relative velocity of approach in a collision.

$$e = \frac{v_2 - v_1}{u_1 - u_2}, \tag{4-10}$$

where e has the value unity for a perfectly elastic collision, but less than one for an inelastic collision. Kinetic energy is conserved in a

Fig. 4-12. Change of velocities in a collision.

perfectly elastic collision, but in inelastic collision, the kinetic energy after impact is less than that before.

Example: An atomic particle of mass m_1 has an initial speed u_1. It experiences an elastic collision with a particle of mass m_2 initially at rest. Find the velocities of projectile and target particles, v_1 and v_2, respectively, after the collision.

$$m_1 u_1^2 = m_1 v_1^2 + m_2 v_2^2 \quad \text{(conservation of energy)},$$

$$m_1 u_1 = -m_1 v_1 + m_2 v_2 \quad \text{(conservation of momentum)},$$

$$v_2 = \frac{m_1 u_1 + m_1 v_1}{m_2},$$

$$m_1 u_1^2 = m_1 v_1^2 + m_2 (m_1^2 u_1^2 + 2 m_1^2 u_1 v_1 + m_1^2 v_1^2)/m_2^2,$$

$$- v_1^2 (m_1 + m_2) - 2 m_1 u_1 v_1 + u_1^2 (m_2 - m_1) = 0,$$

$$v_1 = u_1 \frac{m_1 - m_2}{m_1 + m_2} \quad \text{and} \quad v_2 = u_1 \frac{2 m_1}{m_1 + m_2}.$$

PROBLEMS

Uniform circular motion

4-32. A 2.0-lb stone, to which is attached a cord, is whirled in a horizontal circle of radius 3.0 ft. If the tensile strength of the cord is 20 lb, what is the maximum speed the stone can have in the circle? (*Ans*: 0.82 rev/sec)

4-33. A small 40-gm block revolves in a horizontal circle on a frictionless table top, at the end of a cord 45 cm long attached to a pin fastened in the table top. The angular speed of the block is 3.0 rad/sec. Calculate (a) the linear speed of the block, (b) the tension in the cord, (c) the kinetic energy of the block. (d) How long would it take for the block to come to rest if it were decelerated at the rate of 2.0 rad/sec²?

4-34. A stone weighing 2.0 lb is whirled in a vertical circle of 3.0-ft radius by means of an attached cord. If the speed of the stone at the bottom of the circle is 25 ft/sec, what is (a) the speed at the top of the circle, (b) the tension in the cord when the stone is at the bottom of the circle? (*Ans*: 5 ft/sec, 15 lb)

4-35. Determine the minimum speed that a pail of water must have to swing in a vertical circle of radius 3.78 ft without spilling. (*Ans*: 11 ft/sec)

4-36. A 5.0-lb ball (Fig. 4-13) rotates in a vertical circle of radius 4.0 ft so that the tension is 1.0 lb in the string when the ball is at position *A* at the top of the circle. Find the tensions at positions *B*, *C*, and *D*. (*Ans*: 6.0 lb, 8.5 lb, 11.0 lb)

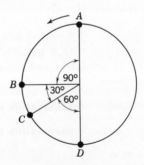

Fig. 4-13

4-37. (a) A car initially at rest on a track rolls down from a height *H* and then goes up around a vertical circle of radius *R*. If the car is not to fall off the track at the top of the circle, what is its minimum speed there? (b) What is the smallest possible value of *H* if the car is not to fall off the track at the top of the circle?

4-38. Find the time of revolution of the earth which would cause bodies to have no apparent weight at the equator. (*Ans*: 1.4 hr)

Conical pendulum

4-39. A 5.0-gm ball hangs from the ceiling on the end of a string 40.0 cm in length. It moves in a horizontal circle with angular speed 7.0 rad/sec. Find the tension in the string.

4-40. A 50.0-lb load swings in a horizontal circle at the end of a 10.0-ft cable. What must be the speed of the load for the cable to maintain a 20° angle with the vertical? What is the tension in the cable? (*Ans:* 6.30 ft/sec, 53.4 lb)

Banking of turns

4-41. A 2800-lb car traveling at 40 mi/hr comes to a curve in the road. If the radius of the curve is 160 ft, find (a) the necessary force to make the car round the curve, (b) the angle at which the road should be banked so that it is not necessary to rely on road friction.

4-42. A curve of 600-ft radius on a level road is banked at the correct angle for a speed of 30 mi/hr. If an automobile rounds this curve at a speed of 60 mi/hr, what is the minimum coefficient of friction (Chapter 3) between tires and road so that the automobile will not skid? Assume all forces to act at the center of mass.

Momentum; impulse

4-43. A 1500-kg automobile moving at a speed of 20 m/sec crashes into a rock wall and is brought to rest in a distance of 40 cm. (a) What is the negative acceleration of the automobile? (b) How long does it take to come to rest? (c) What is the initial momentum? (d) What is the final momentum? (e) What is the change in momentum? (f) What impulse acts on the automobile? (g) What average force acts on the automobile during the collision? (*Ans:* $-\overline{5}00$ m/sec²; 1/25 sec; $3\overline{0},000$ kg m/sec; 0; $3\overline{0},000$ kg m/sec; $3\overline{0},000$ kg m/sec; $7\overline{5}0,000$ kg m/sec² (or newtons).)

4-44. A 1.00-kg body initially at rest is acted upon by a force of 50.0 newtons and acquires a speed of 0.100 m/sec. (a) During what time did the force act? (b) What was the impulse? (*Ans:* 0.00200 sec; 0.100 newton-sec)

4-45. A field gun fires a 20-kg shell. It has to move 2.0 m on the inside of the gun and emerges with a speed of 300 m/sec. (a) What was the final momentum of the shell? (b) What average force acted to accelerate it in the barrel? (*Ans:* $6\overline{0}00$ kg-m/sec; 4.5×10^5 newton)

4-46. A 2.0-oz bullet is fired horizontally at a 4.0-lb block resting on a horizontal smooth surface. The bullet is embedded in the block. (a) If the initial speed of the bullet is 1200 ft/sec, what is the speed of block and bullet after impact? (b) What fraction of the initial kinetic energy is lost in impact? (*Ans:* 36 ft/sec; 97%)

4-47. A 96.0-lb body is initially at rest. It is given a blow of impulse 50.0 lb-sec. What speed does the body acquire?

4-48. Show that when a moving particle collides with a stationary particle that is either k or $1/k$ times as massive, it transfers to the stationary particle the fraction $4k/(1 + k)^2$ of its kinetic energy. Assume a head-on, perfectly elastic collision.

4-49. A situation on a pool table is shown in Fig. 4-14. The balls are 2.00 in. in diameter, and the coefficient of restitution between a ball and the rail is 0.90. If the cue ball C is to hit the 4-ball on the first rebound from the far rail and drive the 4-ball squarely into the pocket without hitting any other balls, with what angle θ to the normal of the near rail must the cue ball be directed? The cue ball is hit straight, without any "English." (*Ans:* 50.3°)

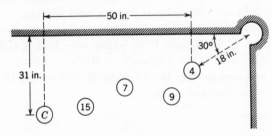

Fig. 4-14

4-50. A golf ball driven 200 yd landed on a horizontal rock and bounced 50 yd. What was the coefficient of restitution of the ball on the rock? (Neglect spin of ball.) (*Ans:* 1/4)

4-51. A heavy slab is set at an angle θ with the horizontal. A ball is dropped onto the slab and is observed to rebound from the slab in a horizontal direction. (a) What is the value of the coefficient of restitution between the ball and the slab? (b) How much energy was lost, in terms of θ and v, where v is the original velocity? (*Ans:* $\tan^2 \theta$; $\frac{1}{2} mv^2 (1 - \tan^2 \theta)$)

4-52. A billiard ball rolls on a smooth floor with a speed of 100 cm/sec. It strikes a smooth wall near the corner (see Fig. 4-15) at an

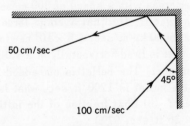

Fig. 4-15

angle of 45 °, and after rebounding from the second wall its speed is reduced to 50 cm/sec. Find (a) the coefficient of restitution between ball and wall, and (b) the final direction of motion of the ball. (*Ans*: 1/2; 45 °)

4-53. A cue ball moving with velocity v strikes another billiard ball of equal mass, initially at rest. The line of centers at impact makes an angle of 30.0 ° with v. If the second ball moves at a speed of $0.823 v$ after impact, what is the coefficient of restitution and what is the velocity of the cue ball after impact? (Neglect friction and effects of rotation.) (*Ans*: 0.9; $0.502 v$ at 48.8 ° with original v)

4-54. A uranium nucleus of mass 4.0×10^{-22} gm is moving along the x-axis with a speed of 1.0×10^9 cm/sec when it explodes into two equal fragments of 2.0×10^{-22} gm each. Both fragments stay on the x-axis. If the explosion gives 2.0×10^{-4} erg of energy to the system, find the final velocities of the fragments. (*Ans*: 1.7×10^9 cm/sec, 0.3×10^9 cm/sec)

4-55. A 10-gm ball with a velocity of 300 cm/sec makes direct impact with a stationary ball of mass 30 gm. After impact, the velocity of the smaller ball is zero. (a) What is the coefficient of restitution and what is the velocity imparted to the larger ball? (b) What is the fractional loss in kinetic energy? (*Ans*: 1/3; 100 cm/sec; 2/3)

4-56. Cornell is playing Princeton. A 180-lb back dives over the line at a speed of 30 ft/sec and is tackled in midair by a 300-lb linesman moving in the opposite direction at 20 ft/sec. (a) What is the speed and direction of the players immediately after impact? (b) If the time of impact is 1/10 sec, what is the average force exerted by one player on the other? (*Ans*: Linesman moves forward 1.2 ft/sec, $\overline{1700}$ lb)

4-57. A 1000-lb bomb is dropped from an airplane flying horizontally at 225 mi/hr at an altitude of 3025 ft. The ground which it strikes offers an average resistance to the bomb of 3.5×10^5 lb. For what interval should the time fuse in the nose of the bomb be set so that the bomb shall explode just as it comes to rest, if the fuse is detonated on impact? Neglect air resistance. (*Ans*: 0.049 sec)

4-58. A 1.0-lb ball of modeling clay moving northward with a speed of 20 ft/sec collides with a like ball of modeling clay moving eastward with a speed of 20 ft/sec. Compute (a) the total momentum of the two after collision, (b) the total kinetic energy after collision. (*Ans*: 0.87 slug-ft, 6.3 ft-lb)

4-59. A 10-lb shell is fired vertically upward and explodes at its maximum height of 1600 ft into two fragments of 2.0 lb and 8.0 lb. Both fragments strike the ground at the same instant, and the 8-lb fragment is observed to strike at a horizontal distance of 100 ft NE from the point from which it was fired. (a) Where did the 2-lb fragment strike? (b) What was the horizontal component of the velocity of the 2-lb fragment? (*Ans*: 400 ft SW from origin; 40 ft/sec, SW)

4-60. A nucleus, originally at rest, decays radioactively by emitting an electron of momentum 9.22×10^{-16} gm-cm/sec. At right angles to the direction of the electron, a neutrino is emitted with momentum 5.33×10^{-16} gm-cm/sec. (a) In what direction does the residual nucleus recoil? (b) What is its momentum? (c) If the mass of the residual nucleus is 3.90×10^{-22} gm, what is its kinetic energy?

4-61. A hailstorm is falling at an angle of $45°$. The individual hailstones weigh 1.0×10^{-4} kg each and travel with a speed of 7.0 m/sec. 2800 hailstones strike the vertical wall of a barn each second. The barn is 14 m long and 10 m high. (a) What is the change of the horizontal component of momentum in each collision? (b) What is the total horizontal impulse on the side of the barn in one second? (c) What is the average force on the side of the barn? How is this related to the "pressure" on the barn? (d) Compare this situation with the kinetic theory of gas pressure, indicating as many similarities and differences as you can think of.

CHAPTER 5

Work and Energy

The *work* done by any agent on a body is the product of force and displacement of the body in the direction of the force:

$$\text{work} = Fs. \tag{5-1}$$

The *foot-pound* is the work done by a force of 1 lb exerted through a distance of 1 ft. The *erg* is the work done by a force of 1 dyne exerted through a distance of 1 cm. A *joule* is 10^7 ergs. The *newton-meter* is the work done by a force of 1 newton exerted through a distance of 1 meter.

Whenever one body slides upon another, some work is done against a frictional force between them. The *frictional force* F is proportional to the normal force N pressing the two surfaces together, and F is directed parallel to these surfaces:

$$F = \mu N. \tag{5-2}$$

The coefficient of friction μ is defined as the ratio of the frictional force to the normal force. The coefficient of static friction μ_s may be calculated from the limiting angle of repose (Fig. 5-1). Sliding friction is less than static friction, and rolling friction is less than sliding friction.

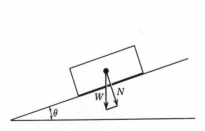

Fig. 5-1. $\mu_s = \tan \theta.$

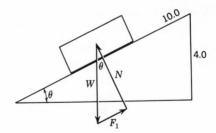

Fig. 5-2

Example: What force parallel to the incline (Fig. 5-2) is required to give a body of mass 50.0 kg an acceleration of 10 m/sec² up an inclined plane which rises 4.0 m in each 10.0 m of the incline, if the coefficient of friction between the sliding body and the incline is 0.20?

$$\frac{F_1}{mg} = \frac{4.0 \text{ m}}{10.0 \text{ m}}.$$

Force to hold block stationary on smooth plane: $F_1 = 196$ newtons,

$$N = W \cos 23° \ 30' = 9.8 \times 50 \times 0.917 = 449 \text{ newtons}.$$

Force to overcome sliding friction: $F_2 = \mu N = 0.20 \times 449 = 90$ newtons,

$$F = ma = 50.0 \text{ kg} \times 10.0 \text{ m/sec}^2 = 500 \text{ newtons}.$$

Net force to accelerate block: $F_3 = 500$ newtons.
Total force applied parallel to plane: $F = 196 + 90 + 500 = 786$ newtons.

Energy is the capacity for doing work. *Potential energy* is energy of position or configuration. For gravitational potential energy,

$$\text{PE} = Wh \quad \text{or} \quad \text{PE} = mgh. \tag{5-3}$$

Kinetic energy is energy of motion:

$$\text{KE} = \tfrac{1}{2} mv^2. \tag{5-4}$$

For transformations between work and kinetic energy:

$$Fs = \tfrac{1}{2} mv^2. \tag{5-5}$$

Energy can be neither created nor destroyed, but only transformed. This is the *principle of conservation of energy.* Expressed differently, the total amount of energy in the universe remains constant.

Example: Find the maximum speed acquired by a pendulum when the bob is released from point B in Fig. 5-3.

When the bob is pulled aside from its lowest position O to the point B, it is raised a distance h and is given potential energy Wh. When the bob is released, it moves toward O. Its energy, while constant, changes from potential to kinetic, the sum of the two forms always being equal to Wh. At point O, all the energy is kinetic. The speed of the bob can be obtained from

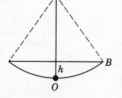

Fig. 5-3

$$Wh = \frac{1}{2} mv^2 = \frac{1}{2} \frac{W}{g} v^2,$$

$$v = \sqrt{2gh}.$$

A *machine* is a device for applying energy at man's convenience. The *actual mechanical advantage* (AMA) of a machine is the ratio of the output force F_o to the input force F_i applied to the machine:

$$\text{AMA} = \frac{F_o}{F_i}. \tag{5-6}$$

The *ideal mechanical advantage* (IMA) of a machine is defined as the ratio of the distance s_i through which the input force acts to the distance s_o through which the output force acts:

$$\text{IMA} = \frac{s_i}{s_o}. \tag{5-7}$$

The *efficiency* of a machine is defined as the ratio of the work output to the work input:

$$\text{efficiency} = \frac{\text{work output}}{\text{work input}} = \frac{F_o s_o}{F_i s_i} = \frac{\text{AMA}}{\text{IMA}}. \tag{5-8}$$

Power is the time rate of doing work:

$$P = \frac{\text{work}}{t} = \frac{Fs}{t} = F\bar{v}. \tag{5-9}$$

One horsepower is 550 ft-lb/sec or 33,000 ft-lb/min. *One watt* is 1 joule/sec. One horsepower is equivalent to 746 watts.

Example: A 1000-lb box is lifted a distance of 10 ft, with a pulley system, by the application of a force of 150 lb for a distance of 80 ft. Find (a) the actual mechanical advantage, (b) the ideal mechanical advantage, and (c) the efficiency of the pulley system.

$$\text{AMA} = \frac{F_o}{F_i} = \frac{1000 \text{ lb}}{150 \text{ lb}} = 6.7.$$

$$\text{IMA} = \frac{s_i}{s_o} = \frac{80 \text{ ft}}{10 \text{ ft}} = 8.0.$$

$$\text{efficiency} = \frac{F_o s_o}{F_i s_i} = \frac{(1000 \text{ lb})(10 \text{ ft})}{(150 \text{ lb})(80 \text{ ft})} = 0.83 = 83\%.$$

or

$$\text{efficiency} = \text{AMA/IMA} = \frac{6.7}{8.0} = 0.83 = 83\%.$$

Example: A ski tow (Fig. 5-4) is to be oper-
ated on a 37° slope 800 ft long. The rope is to
move 8.0 mi/hr and power must be provided for 80
riders at one time, each weighing, on the average, 150 lb. Estimate the horsepower required
to operate the tow.

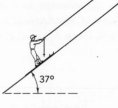

Fig. 5-4

Work to raise one rider, against gravity equals

$mgh = W$ 800 ft sin 37°

$= 150$ lb (800 ft) (0.602) = 72,000 ft-lb.

Time equals

$$\frac{s}{v} = \frac{800 \text{ ft} \; 3600 \text{ sec/hr}}{8.0 \text{ mi/hr} \; 5280 \text{ ft/mi}} = 68 \text{ sec}.$$

Power to raise one rider (assuming no losses) =

$$\frac{72,000 \text{ ft-lb}}{68 \text{ sec}} \times \frac{\text{sec hp}}{550 \text{ ft-lb}} = 1.9 \text{ hp}.$$

Power to raise 80 riders (assuming no losses) = $80 \times 1.9 = 1\overline{5}0$ hp.

Assuming a 30% power loss due to friction, total power required =
$1.3 \times 1\overline{5}0 = 2\overline{0}0$ hp = $1\overline{6}0$ kw.

PROBLEMS

Work

5-1. A 16-lb shot is lying on the ground at one corner of a playing
field. The playing field is square, 60 ft on a side, and has a fence 5.0
ft high bordering it. A janitor carries the shot to the extreme opposite
corner and lifts it over the fence. (a) What amount of total work does the
janitor do? (b) How much kinetic energy does the shot have just before it
hits a bench which is 2.0 ft off the ground on the other side of the fence?

5-2. A halfback, while throwing a quick pass, pushes on the ball with
a constant force for 0.10 sec, while he moves his hand forward a distance
of 3.2 ft. The ball weighs 2.0 lb. (a) What was the acceleration of the
ball? (b) What was the force exerted on the ball? (c) How much work
was done on the ball? (d) What power was developed by the back while
accelerating the ball? (*Ans:* $6\overline{4}0$ ft/sec²; 40 lb; $1\overline{3}0$ ft-lb; 2.3 hp)

5-3. How much work is necessary to accelerate a 1600-lb automobile
from 20 mi/hr to 30 mi/hr?

5-4. A rifle bullet of mass 10 gm strikes and embeds itself in a block
of mass 990 gm which rests on a horizontal frictionless surface. The impact compresses by 10 cm a coil spring between the block and a fixed

wall. Calibration of the spring shows that a force of 100,000 dynes is required to compress the spring 1.0 cm. (a) Find the maximum potential energy of the spring. (b) Find the velocity of the block just after impact. (c) What was the initial velocity of the bullet? (*Ans:* 0.50 joule; 100 cm/sec; 10 m/sec)

Energy

5-5. A package weighing 64 lb slid off the end of a chute with a speed of 12 ft/sec. Determine its kinetic energy.

5-6. To demonstrate the effects of centrifugal reaction, a 12-kg bucket of water is swung rapidly at arm's length in a circle of radius 90 cm, in a vertical plane, with angular speed 4.0 rad/sec. (a) What is the linear speed of the bucket? (b) What is the kinetic energy of the bucket of water? (c) What force must the demonstrator exert on the bucket to keep it in its circular path at the instant it passes its lowest point? (d) at its highest point? (*Ans:* 3$\overline{6}$0 cm/sec; 0.77 joule; 2$\overline{9}$0 newtons; 55 newtons)

Transformation of energy

5-7. A loaded truck weighing 6.0 tons and traveling 45 mi/hr is stopped with the brakes in 10 sec. How much heat (joules) is developed?

5-8. Water flowing over a large dam has a sheer drop of 500 ft. If 75% of the loss in gravitational potential energy is converted into heat, how much warmer is the water at the foot of the dam than the water at the top? (*Ans:* 0.5°F)

Work against gravity

5-9. A block of mass m is projected up a smooth inclined plane of slope angle α with an initial velocity v_0. How far up the plane will it slide?

5-10. What is the maximum value of h from which the car in Fig. 5-5 can be released if it is not to leave the track at point A where the curve of radius r begins? The track is frictionless. (*Ans:* $(3\sqrt{3}/4)r$)

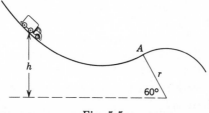

Fig. 5-5

5-11. A 20.0-gm bullet is fired into a ballistic pendulum of mass 6.00 gm. The center of gravity of the pendulum rises 10.0 cm after the pendulum is struck. Find the initial speed of the bullet.

5-12. A guided missile weighing 12 tons is fired vertically, using a propellant which exerts a thrust of 33 tons for 10 sec. Determine the maximum height to which it will rise, assuming g to be 32 ft/sec². (*Ans:* $\overline{16},500$ ft)

5-13. A body of mass m slides down an inclined plane of length l and height h, with coefficient of friction μ. It starts from rest at the top of the incline. How fast will the body be going when it reaches the bottom?

5-14. A stunt rider rides a small cart down an incline onto a vertical circular track having a diameter of 30.0 ft. From what height above the bottom of the loop must he start to just stay on the track around the loop? (*Ans:* 37.5 ft)

Friction

5-15. A boy finds that he can just drag a 100-lb load by exerting a 30-lb tension on a rope which makes an angle of 30° with the horizontal. If he lowers the rope to make a 20° angle with the horizontal and continues to exert the 30-lb force for 2.0 min, find (a) the work done by the boy, (b) the work done against friction, (c) the kinetic energy of the load.

5-16. A 10-lb block is placed on an incline. The coefficient of friction between block and incline is 0.36. Find (a) the angle of repose, (b) the resultant force on the block if the incline is raised to 30°, (c) the acceleration of the block in part (b). (*Ans:* 20°, 1.9 lb, 6.1 ft/sec²)

5-17. An inclined plane is 130 cm long and its upper end is 50 cm above the level of the lower end (Fig. 5-6). The block m_2 rests on the plane, and has a mass of 200 gm. The block m_1 rests on m_2 and has a mass of 60 gm. The coefficient of static friction between the two blocks is 0.50; the coefficient of sliding friction between the lower block and the plane is 0.33. A force F upward and parallel to the plane is applied to the lower block. (a) What is the acceleration of the lower block when the upper block just starts to slip on it? (b) What is the maximum value of F before this slipping takes place? (*Ans:* 75 cm/sec²; 200 gm-wt)

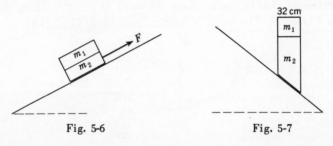

Fig. 5-6   Fig. 5-7

5-18. A block $m_2 = 700$ gm rests on an inclined plane that makes an angle of 36° 52′ with the horizontal (Fig. 5-7). The coefficient of sliding friction between the block and plane is 0.40. On the smooth horizontal top of m_2 rests squarely a block $m_1 = 100$ gm. In the horizontal direction in a plane parallel to the direction of motion the blocks m_1 and m_2 are 32 cm wide. How long after the system is released will block m_1 fall off block m_2? (*Ans:* 0.36 sec)

5-19. A car rounds a curve of radius 40 ft on a level roadway. If the coefficient of static friction between the tires and the road is 0.20, what is the maximum speed with which the car can round the curve without skidding?

5-20. Determine the maximum non-skid speed for an automobile to travel around a flat curve of 500-ft radius if the coefficient of friction is 0.050. (*Ans:* 28 ft/sec)

5-21. A block is placed on a circular disk which is accelerated from rest at the rate of 1.0 rad/sec². If the coefficient of friction between the block and the disk is μ, how far out from the center of the disk was the block, if it begins to move 1.0 sec after the disk begins to accelerate?

5-22. If the coefficient of static friction between the tires and the road is μ_s, show that the minimum stopping distance for an automobile of mass m and speed v is $v^2/2\mu_s g$.

5-23. A hockey player hits a puck and imparts to it a velocity of 20 ft/sec. How far will the puck slide if the coefficient of friction between it and the ice is 0.05?

5-24. If the coefficient of friction between a book and a wall is 0.25, how hard would one have to push horizontally in order to hold a 1.25-lb book against a vertical wall without having the book start to slip down the wall? (*Ans:* 5.0 lb)

5-25. In Fig. 5-8, what range of accelerations may be given to the cart during which m_2 will not slip on the cart?

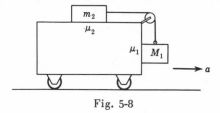

Fig. 5-8

$$\left(Ans:\ \frac{m_1 - \mu_2 m_2}{m_2 + \mu_1 m_1}\ g \leqslant a \leqslant \frac{m_1 + \mu_2 m_2}{m_2 - \mu_1 m_1}\ g \right)$$

5-26. What force is necessary to give a block of mass 2.0 slugs an acceleration of 3.0 ft/sec² horizontally, if the block is resting on the floor of an elevator moving downward with an acceleration of 10 ft/sec²? The coefficient of friction between block and floor is 0.30. (*Ans:* 13 lb)

5-27. Two weightless rings can slide along a rough horizontal rod with coefficient of friction μ (Fig. 5-9). The rings are connected by a light, inextensible string of length a, to the mid-point of which is attached a weight W. Show that the greatest distance between the two rings consistent with the equilibrium of the system is $d = \dfrac{\mu a}{\sqrt{1 + \mu^2}}$.

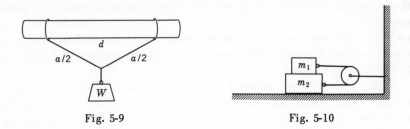

Fig. 5-9   Fig. 5-10

5-28. In Fig. 5-10, what force F must be applied horizontally to m_2 so that m_1 will slide horizontally on m_2 with an acceleration equal to $\frac{3}{13}g$? The pulley is massless and frictionless. (*Ans:* $6\overline{5}0$ gm-wt)

5-29. A block 1.0 cm wide has an initial velocity of 14 cm/sec at a point midway between two walls, toward one of the walls. The walls are 51 cm apart. The floor has a coefficient of friction of 0.0010, and the coefficient of restitution of walls and block is 1.0. How many times does the block hit each wall, and where will it stop?

5-30. A square wire frame with side a is hung on a rough peg with a coefficient of friction μ (Fig. 5-11). How close to the corner of the square is the peg if the square is just about to slip?

5-31. A 1.0-lb plate rests in the middle of a tablecloth-covered table 4.0 ft wide. The coefficient of friction between tablecloth and table is 0.5, between plate and cloth 2.0. With what uniform velocity must the tablecloth be pulled in order that the plate will still remain on the table at the moment the cloth has been removed?

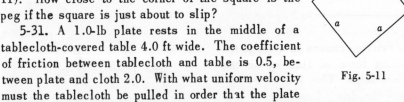

Fig. 5-11

Power

5-32. An unbalanced force of 10 newtons acts on a 20-kg body initially at rest. Compute (a) the work done in the first second, (b) in the third second, and (c) the instantaneous power at the end of the third second. (*Ans:* 2.5 newton-m, 12.5 joules, 15 watts)

5-33. A grinding wheel 5.40 in. in diameter is driven by an electric motor at 1820 rev/min. A tool is sharpened by pressing it against the wheel with a normal force of 1.54 lb. If the coefficient of friction between tool and wheel is 0.324, what horsepower is required to drive the wheel, other frictional forces being neglected?

5-34. An escalator 40 ft long connects one floor with another 25 ft above it. The escalator is designed to carry 120 persons/minute, of average weight 160 lb each, at a constant linear speed of 2.0 ft/sec. (a) How powerful a motor is needed to carry the maximum load? (b) If a 160-lb man walks up the escalator at a uniform velocity so that he reaches the top in 10 sec, what work must the escalator do on him? (c) If the same 160-lb man rides at the middle of the slope, and walks down the escalator at the same rate the escalator moves up (so that he remains in the same place), at what rate must the escalator motor work? (*Ans:* 44 hp; 4̄000 ft-lb; 0.36 hp)

5-35. A coal loader consists of an endless belt, driven by a gasoline engine, which moves coal 36 ft up an incline, lifting it 15 ft vertically. It delivers 12 tons of coal per minute to freight cars. (a) How much work does the machine do in 4.0 min? (b) If the loader has an efficiency of 60%, what must be the minimum horsepower of the driving engine? (c) If the loader were redesigned so as to be 40 ft long and 12 ft high, would the engine required to load coal at the same rate (with same efficiency) be larger or smaller? Why? (*Ans:* 2.6 × 10⁶ ft-lb; 3̄30 hp; smaller)

5-36. A 175-kg pile driver is lifted vertically 5.0 m at each stroke. (a) What is the potential energy at the top of the stroke? (b) The steel cable used to hoist the pile driver has a cross sectional area of 3.0 cm², is of length 12 m, and has a Young's modulus (Chapter 8) of 20×10^{10} newtons/m^2. How much does the cable stretch when the pile driver is momentarily jerked upward with an acceleration of 20.0 m/sec²? (c) Friction causes an average retarding force of 10.0 kg as the driver falls. What kinetic energy does the driver have after it has fallen a distance of 4.0 m? (d) For an over-all efficiency of 75%, what average power must be supplied by the hoist engine if the pile driver is hoisted back to the top in 6.0 sec? (*Ans:* 8̄600 joules; 1.0 cm; 5̄200 joules; 1.9 kw)

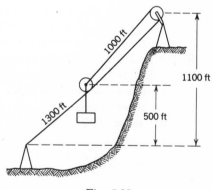

Fig. 5-12

Pulleys

5-37. A telpherage system for transporting ore from a mine is shown in Fig. 5-12. During a trip down with a 3.0-ton load, the hoist was stopped for repairs. At that time, the dimensions were as shown. (a) What was the tension in the supporting cable? (b) What force did the brake have to supply to the hoisting cable? (*Ans:* 9.8 tons; 1.5 tons)

5-38. What is the ideal mechanical advantage of the machine shown in Fig. 5-13? Neglect the mass of the pulleys. (b) By exerting a force $F_i = 25$ lb, a man can lift a weight $W = 60$ lb. What is the efficiency of the machine? (c) How much power does a man deliver to the machine when the 60-lb load is raised at a constant rate of 2.0 ft in 5.0 sec? (*Ans:* 3; 80%; 30 ft-lb/sec)

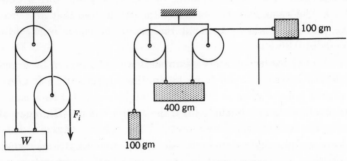

Fig. 5-13   Fig. 5-14

5-39. A painter hoists himself up the side of a tall building by a block and tackle having three sheaves in the upper block and two in the lower block. The man and his equipment weigh 240 lb. What is the tension in the rope?

5-40. In the system shown in Fig. 5-14, if $\mu = 0.50$, for the block and horizontal plane, what is the acceleration of the 400-gm mass? (*Ans:* $5/12 \ g$)

5-41. In Fig. 5-15, blocks A and B are connected by a weightless cord passing over a weightless, frictionless pulley. Block B has a mass of 16 kg and block A a mass of 4.0 kg. The coefficient of sliding friction

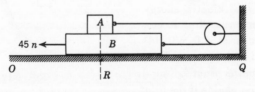

Fig. 5-15

between blocks A and B is 0.25, and between block B and the horizontal surface OQ it is 0.10. A force of 45 newtons is applied to block B parallel to OQ. Use $g = 10$ m/sec^2. (a) Draw two force diagrams, one showing the forces acting on block A, the other showing the forces acting on B. (b) Calculate the acceleration of block A. (c) At time $t = 0$, block A is at point R and is moving to the right with an initial velocity of 5.0 cm/sec.

How much work is done by the agent exerting the 45-newton force during the time interval between $t = 0$ and $t = 0.8$ sec? Assume block B is of sufficient length so that A never falls off. (d) What is the kinetic energy of block A at time $t = 0.8$ sec?

Inclined plane; wedge

5-42. Derive an expression for the efficiency of an inclined plane, in terms of the coefficient of friction and the elevation angle. (*Ans:* $1/(1 + \mu \cot \theta)$)

5-43. A 12-lb block rests on a smooth plane inclined at 30° to the horizontal and is connected by a cord passing over a frictionless pulley to a second block weighing 8.0 lb which hangs vertically. (a) Show in a diagram the complete set of forces acting on each block. (b) Find the acceleration of each block. (c) What is the tension in the cord? (*Ans:* 3.2 ft/sec²; 7.2 lb)

5-44. A 100-lb block is pushed up an inclined plane, making an angle of 30° with the horizontal, by a force of 75 lb parallel to the plane. The top of the plane is 5.0 ft above the base. The coefficient of friction between block and plane is 0.20. Find: (a) the force of friction, (b) the acceleration of the block, (c) the final kinetic energy of the block, (d) the energy expended in friction, (e) the final potential energy of the block. (*Ans:* 17.3 lb, 2.35 ft/sec², 77 ft-lb, 173 ft-lb, 500 ft-lb)

5-45. A type of cam arrangement is shown in Fig. 5-16. The vertical rod, of mass 400 gm, runs through frictionless vertical guides and ends in a frictionless bearing that rests on the incline of the movable wedge.

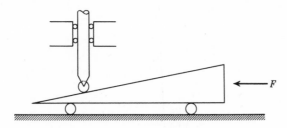

Fig. 5-16

The wedge angle is 9° 28′. The wedge has a mass of 100 gm and runs on frictionless horizontal bearings. A constant force F of 280 gm-wt is applied horizontally to the wedge as shown. What is the acceleration of the vertical rod? (*Ans:* 314 cm/sec²)

5-46. A block of mass 35 lb is projected up a 45° incline of height 10 ft, with an initial speed of 30 ft/sec. When it reaches the top of the incline and strikes a metal stop normally, the coefficient of restitution is $1/\sqrt{2}$. The block slides down the plane, reaching the bottom with a speed of 20 ft/sec. What is the coefficient of friction between the block and the plane? (*Ans:* 0.38)

5-47. Show that the horizontal force F required to start the block of weight W moving up the plane in Fig. 5-17 is

$$F = W \frac{\mu_s \cos \theta + \sin \theta}{\cos \theta - \mu_s \sin \theta},$$

and that the normal force exerted by the plane is

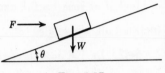

Fig. 5-17

$$N = \frac{W}{\cos \theta - \mu_s \sin \theta}.$$

Show that it is impossible to start a block moving up a plane by a *horizontal* push if the angle of the plane is greater than $\cot^{-1} \mu_s$.

Other machines

5-48. Derive an expression for the ideal mechanical advantage of the differential wheel and axle shown in Fig. 5-18. (*Ans: $2r_2/r_2 - r_1$*)

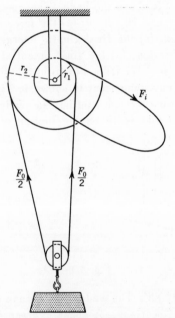

Fig. 5-18

5-49. In the arrangement of Fig. 5-19, the radii of the wheel and axle are 18 in. and 6.0 in. The efficiencies are: lever, 90%; wheel and axle, 80%; pulley system, 60%. Find (a) the IMA and AMA of each individual machine, (b) the IMA and AMA of the combination, (c) the force needed to raise a 1.0-ton load, and (d) the power needed to raise the 1.0-ton load at a rate of 2.0 ft/sec.

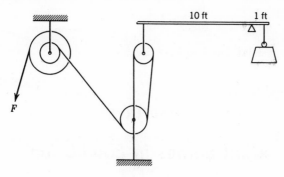

Fig. 5-19

5-50. A screw-type jack with a 3.0-ft handle and a pitch of 5/8 in. is used to raise a load of 5000 lb. The jack has an efficiency of 35% and is being turned at the rate of 40 rev/min. Find (a) the IMA, (b) the AMA, (c) the force needed to operate the jack, (d) the power being supplied to the jack, (e) the power being wasted. (*Ans:* 360, 127, 39 lb, 0.86 hp, 0.55 hp).

CHAPTER 6

Rigid Bodies in Equilibrium

A rigid body can be considered as a collection of particles held in fixed relations to one another. The placement of the forces acting on a body (as well as their magnitudes and directions) must be considered in determining the motion of the body.

The *moment arm* of a force is the perpendicular distance from an axis to the line of action of the force. The *torque* produced by a force is equal to the product of the force and its moment arm:

$$L = Fs. \tag{6-1}$$

Torque is measured in pound-feet or in centimeter-dynes, or any such product of force and distance units. Torque is a vector quantity and is represented by a vector in the direction a right-hand screw would advance if it experienced a torque in the same sense as the body considered.

For an object to be in equilibrium, it is necessary (a) that the vector sum of the forces applied to it be zero, and (b) that the algebraic sum of the torques (about any axis) acting on it be zero:

$$\Sigma F_x = 0, \qquad \Sigma F_y = 0, \qquad \Sigma F_z = 0, \tag{6-2}$$

$$\Sigma L = 0. \tag{6-3}$$

If the forces acting on a body are concurrent forces (forces whose lines of action intersect at a point) the first condition, Eq. (6-2), is sufficient for equilibrium. But if the forces are nonconcurrent, it is necessary to take into account Eq. (6-3) as well.

A *couple* consists of two forces (not in the same line) equal in magnitude and opposite in direction. The torque produced by a couple is equal to the magnitude of one (either) of the forces times the perpendicular distance between them.

Example: A uniform 200-lb beam, 20 ft long, has one end hinged at the wall; the other end is supported by chain AB, which makes a 30° angle with the horizontal beam (Fig. 6-1). A 2000-lb load is hung at the end A of the beam. Find the tension T in chain AB.

Indicate by vectors all the forces acting *on* the 20-ft beam. The force of reaction F of the hinge on the beam is unknown in both direction and magnitude. If we apply the second condition for equilibrium ($\Sigma L = 0$) to an axis through point O, the unknown force F has no moment arm and, therefore, causes no torque. We can thus find tension T without knowing force F.

Torques about O: (200 lb)(10 ft) = $2\overline{0}00$ lb-ft, clockwise;

$\qquad$ 2000 lb(20 ft) = 40,000 lb-ft, clockwise.

$\qquad T(20 \text{ ft})(\sin 30°) = T$ 10 ft, counterclockwise.

$\qquad T(10 \text{ ft}) - 2\overline{0}00 \text{ lb-ft} - 4\overline{0},000 \text{ lb-ft} - F(0) = 0.$

Hence $T = 4\overline{2},000$ lb = 2.1 tons.

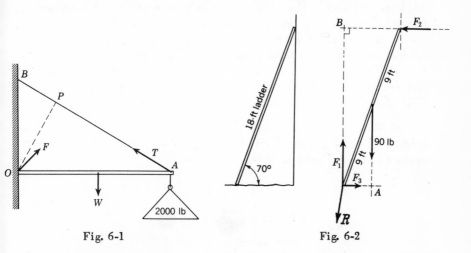

Fig. 6-1 $\qquad\qquad\qquad\qquad\qquad$ Fig. 6-2

Example: A 90-lb uniform ladder 18 ft long leans against a smooth vertical wall (Fig. 6-2). The ladder makes an angle of 70° with the ground. Find the forces the ladder exerts against the wall and the ground.

Represent by vectors each force acting on the ladder. Its weight, 90 lb, is directed downward at the mid-point of the ladder. The reaction force F_2 exerted by the wall on the ladder is horizontal, since the wall was assumed frictionless. Force F_1 is the vertical reaction of the ground, and F_3 is the frictional force at the ground. Apply the conditions for equilibrium.

From $\Sigma F = 0$,

$$F_3 - F_2 = 0 \text{ and } F_1 - 90 \text{ lb} = 0.$$

For torques about point O, $\Sigma L = 0$ gives

$$90 \text{ lb } (OA) - F_2 (OB) = 0,$$

or

$$90 \text{ lb } (9 \text{ ft cos } 70°) - F_2 (18 \text{ ft sin } 70°) = 0.$$

Solve these equations simultaneously to obtain

$$F_1 = 90 \text{ lb}, \ F_2 = F_3 = 45 \text{ lb tan } 70° = 16.4 \text{ lb}.$$

Hence the force exerted by the ladder on the wall is 90 lb, perpendicular to the wall. The resultant push of the ladder against the ground is $R = (16.4^2 + 90^2)^{\frac{1}{2}} = 92$ lb, and the angle this force makes with the ground is $\tan^{-1} (90/16.4) = 80°$.

The earth's attraction for a body is exerted on each particle of matter the body contains. The weight of a body is a system of (very nearly) parallel forces acting on the individual particles. There is a point, called the *center of gravity* of the body, about which the body will balance, whatever its orientation: $\Sigma w_i x_i = 0$, where w_i is the weight of an individual particle and x_i is the lever arm of force w_i measured to the center of gravity. Hence the weight of a body can be represented by a single force acting downward at the center of gravity.

Example: A weightless bar carries two small masses which have weights W_1 and W_2, respectively (Fig. 6-3). Find their center of gravity, measured from the fixed point O.

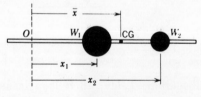

Fig. 6-3

The resultant force or weight of the system is

$$W = W_1 + W_2.$$

By equating the torques about point O, we find

$$W\bar{x} = W_1 x_1 + W_2 x_2.$$

Hence the center of gravity is distant from O by

$$\bar{x} = \frac{W_1 x_1 + W_2 x_2}{W_1 + W_2}.$$

(*Note:* If the origin of coordinates is taken at the center of gravity, $\bar{x} = 0$ and $-x_1/x_2 = W_2/W_1$, showing that the center of gravity of two point masses is a point that divides the distance between them in the inverse ratio of their weights.)

The center of gravity of a symmetrical body is at its geometric center, provided the material of the body is of uniform density.

For a rigid body, there is a fixed point called the *center of mass* C such that the rigid body moves under the action of external forces as if all its mass m were concentrated at C, and as if all the forces were applied at C.

The coordinates of the center of mass are given by

$$\bar{x} = \frac{1}{m} \sum_i m_i x_i, \qquad \bar{y} = \frac{1}{m} \sum_i m_i y_i, \qquad \bar{z} = \frac{1}{m} \sum_i m_i z_i. \qquad (6\text{-}4)$$

The coordinates of the center of gravity are given by

$$\bar{x} = \frac{\sum_i W_i x_i}{\sum_i W_i}, \qquad \bar{y} = \frac{\sum_i W_i y_i}{\sum_i W_i}, \qquad \bar{z} = \frac{\sum_i W_i z_i}{\sum_i W_i}. \qquad (6\text{-}5)$$

If $W_i = m_i g$ = a constant, the center of mass is identical with the center of gravity. But this is not always true; for very large bodies, g is not the same at every particle.

Example: Find the center of mass of a hemisphere of uniform density ρ (Fig. 6-4).

Consider a circular slab of thickness dx and radius y, whose area is $\pi y^2 = \pi(a^2 - x^2)$. Hence

$$\bar{x} = \frac{\int_0^a x\pi(a^2 - x^2)dx\,\rho}{m} = \frac{\pi\rho a^4}{4m}.$$

But $m = \frac{1}{2}(\frac{4}{3}\pi a^3)\rho$; hence $\bar{x} = \frac{3}{8} a$ and, from symmetry, $\bar{y} = \bar{z} = 0$.

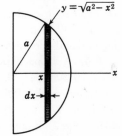

Fig. 6-4

A body is said to be in stable equilibrium [Fig. 6-5(a)] if, when it is displaced slightly, a restoring force or torque tends to return it to its original position, in neutral equilibrium (b) if no force or couple is brought into play, or in unstable equilibrium (c) if a slight displacement produces a force or couple which increases the displacement.

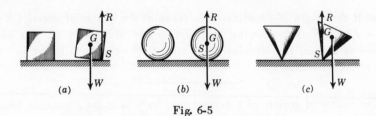

Fig. 6-5

PROBLEMS

6-1. (a) Discuss in general the methods of analyzing a system of forces known to be in equilibrium. (b) Define the term "couple," and show how it is possible to restore equilibrium to a system which was in equilibrium before the couple was applied. (c) If a system of parallel forces on a body is in equilibrium, discuss how to restore equilibrium when a single force at $45°$ to the other forces is applied. *Note*: In (b) and (c), it is not considered an adequate answer to remove the offending couple or force; some other force or forces must be used than those exactly equal in magnitude and opposite in direction to the ones which upset the equilibrium.

6-2. Given only a meter stick, some string, and a body of mass 100-gm, (a) how would you determine the mass of the uniform meter stick? (b) Given another body also, how would you determine the mass? (c) Given also two containers of water, how would you determine which of the two given bodies has the greater density in one simple operation and without calculation?

Bridge, balance

6-3. A bridge 100 ft long weighs 20 tons. Its center of gravity is at its geometric center. A 3000-lb car is 20 ft from one end of the bridge and a 7500-lb truck is 40 ft from the other end of the bridge. Calculate the vertical forces exerted on the bridge by the two supports at its ends.

6-4. A beam balance in good adjustment is balancing a specimen of mass 10.208 gm. On the right pan are the following masses: 10.000 gm, 0.200 gm, and 0.005 gm. The rider is on the beam at the 3-mg mark, which is 1/4 the distance from the center knife edge to the right pan knife edge. Hence the mass of the rider can be calculated to be how many grams? (*Ans:* 0.012 gm)

6-5. A stick 2 m in length is loaded as follows: 1000 gm at 0 cm, 700 gm at 40 cm, 800 gm at 120 cm, and 1500 gm at 200 cm. The stick (of negligible weight) is supported at two points located at the 60-cm mark and the 180-cm mark, in a horizontal position. Find the upward force at each of the two supports.

6-6. A uniform beam 20 ft long is supported in a horizontal position, at each end. The beam weighs 160 lb. A 140-lb boy sits on the beam at a distance of 6.0 ft from one end. (a) What weight is carried by the support at the end of the beam nearer the boy? (b) Where is the center of gravity of the combined weight of the beam and the boy? (*Ans: $F_1 = 178$ lb; 8.1 ft from F_1*)

6-7. A three-panel truss is so constructed of weightless, rigid members that each panel forms an equilateral triangle (Fig. 6-6). A load of

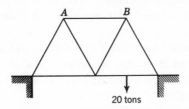

Fig. 6-6

20 tons is suspended from the center of one of the panels as shown. Find the force in the top member AB and specify whether it is tension or compression. (*Ans: 5.8 ton wt. compression*)

Upset force

6-8. A 300-lb cubical crate 6.0 ft wide rests on a horizontal floor against a small obstacle along one edge. In order to overturn the crate most easily, where should one push, and what minimum force must be applied? (*Ans:* 106 lb, applied at upper edge further from obstacle, and in a direction 90° from the diagonal of the crate)

6-9. Five cubes 10 ft on a side are fastened together as shown in Fig. 6-7. The mass of the body is 0.22 slug. It is acted upon by a force F. What value must F have in order that the body will just tip? It is on a smooth floor.

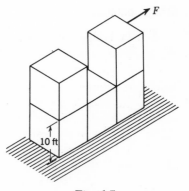

Fig. 6-7

6-10. If it is desired to upset a tall column by a rope of given length pulled from the ground, where should it be applied if the length of the rope is (a) equal to, (b) twice, the height of the column?

Boom

6-11. A 30.0-lb uniform beam 16.0 ft long is hinged to a vertical pole. The beam is held in a horizontal position by a rope reaching from the outer end of the beam to a point on the pole 12.0 ft above the hinge. A load of 60.0 lb is hung from the outer end of the beam. (a) Draw a sketch showing all the forces acting on the beam. (b) Find the horizontal and vertical components of force acting at the hinge, and (c) the tension in the rope. (*Ans:* 100 lb, 15 lb, 125 lb)

6-12. A 20-ft beam, AC, weighing 100 lb is hinged at A to a vertical pole, making an angle of 30° with the pole. A rope extends from end C of the beam to point B on the pole. Angle ABC is 60°, angle BCA is 90°. A load W is hung from point C. (a) If the cable BC has a breaking strength of 250 lb, what is the maximum value that the weight W can have? (b) Write down the three equations required for the equilibrium of the beam. (*Ans:* 4$\overline{5}$0 lb)

6-13. A derrick consists of a vertical mast, or king post, 25 ft tall, and a uniform boom 10 ft long weighing 100 lb. One end of the boom is pivoted 5 ft up from the base of the king post and the far end is held up by a tie rope leading to the top of the king post. If a 900-lb load hangs from the far end of the boom and the boom is held in a horizontal position, find the magnitude of (a) the tension in the tie rope, and (b) the force exerted by the boom on the king post.

6-14. The boom in Fig. 6-8 is uniform and weighs 30 lb. (a) Draw a force diagram showing the forces acting on the boom. (b) Calculate the tension in the supporting wire. Pin A is frictionless. (*Ans:* 100 lb)

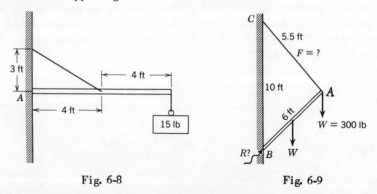

Fig. 6-8   Fig. 6-9

6-15. In the crane of Fig. 6-9, the boom AB is considered to be of negligible weight, $W = 300$ lb, $AB = 6$ ft, $AC = 5.5$ ft, $BC = 10$ ft. Find the tension F in AC, and the hinge reaction force R at B.

6-16. In the crane of prob. 6-15, all dimensions and loads remain the same except that the beam is now one of 400-lb weight with its center of gravity exactly at its middle. Find (a) the tension F, and (b) the hinge reaction force R. (*Ans:* 249 lb, 612 lb, 20.5° from vertical)

6-17. In the arrangement shown in Fig. 6-10, a boom 8.0 ft long is supported by a guy wire, and has at its end a pulley by which a 600-lb load can be raised or lowered. The rope supporting the load runs over the pulley and is carried parallel to the boom back to another pulley near the wall to a fastening. If the maximum compressional load the boom can withstand without buckling is 400 lb/in.², what is the minimum safe cross-sectional area of the boom? (*Ans:* 3.5 in.²)

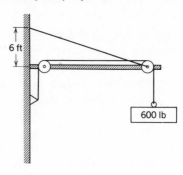

Ladder

Fig. 6-10

6-18. A ladder that is 30 ft long weighs 60 lb. It is leaned against a smooth building in such a way that the ladder makes an angle of 60° with the horizontal. What is the force of the ladder on the building? (*Ans:* 17 lb)

6-19. A uniform bar with rounded ends and length s is hung from one end against a vertical wall by a string of length s. If the free end of the bar is placed against the wall, it is found by repeated experiments that the smallest angle θ that can be made between the bar and the wall is 75° if the bar is to stay in place, without falling. What is the coefficient of friction between bar and wall? (*Ans:* 0.81)

6-20. A 30-ft uniform ladder weighing 50 lb stands on level ground and leans against a smooth vertical wall, making an angle of 70° with the ground. Find the minimum coefficient of friction between ladder and ground that will permit a 150-lb man to stand upright on a rung 20 ft above the ground. (*Ans:* 0.23)

6-21. A uniform ladder 50 ft long is leaning against a smooth wall; the base of the ladder is 30 ft from the foot of the wall. The coefficient of friction between ladder and ground is 0.25. If the ladder weighs 40 lb and a 50-lb load is suspended at a point 5 ft up the ladder, how far can a 150-lb man walk up the ladder before it starts to slip?

6-22. A boy leans a 2.0-lb, 30-in. baseball bat against a wall so that the top of the bat meets the wall 24 in. from the floor. The center of gravity of the bat is 10 in. from the lower end. The horizontal force exerted by the floor (friction) is 1/4 lb. Will the bat remain at rest, or will it slide down, assuming the wall exerts no frictional force on the bat? Explain. (*Ans:* Slides)

Center of gravity

6-23. A square sheet of metal is divided by its two diagonals into four triangles. One of the triangles is now cut away. Find the position of the center of gravity of the piece which remains. (*Ans:* On the bisector of the missing triangle, 7/18 of the width of the square)

6-24. When only the two front wheels of an empty four-wheel truck are on the platform of a scale the scale reads 3500 lb; when only the two rear wheels are on the scale the reading is 2500 lb. The wheel base of the truck is 14.0 ft. How far is the center of gravity from the rear axle? (*Ans:* 8.2 ft)

6-25. Where is the center of mass of a hemispherical bowl of uniform density d, thickness t, and radius R; where $R \gg t$?

6-26. A uniform shaft 8.0 ft long and weighing 60 lb has a 35-lb pulley at one end and another pulley weighing 50 lb a distance 2.5 ft from the other end. Find the center of mass of the system. (*Ans:* 3.6 ft from the 35-lb pulley)

6-27. Find the center of mass of a right circular cylinder of height h with a density which increases uniformly from top to bottom (Fig. 6-11). The density at the top is ρ, and at the bottom it is 2ρ.

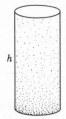

h

6-28. A wheel of fortune was originally made of uniform material of density 1.0 lb/ft² of surface area. In an attempt to "fix" the wheel, an operator cut a hole 6.0 in. in diameter, 1.0 ft from the center of the wheel, and filled the hole with material 1/3 as dense as the original material. A later operator further "fixed" the wheel by mounting on its rear surface a mass of 4.0 oz, 6.0 in. from the center of the wheel. The radius vector to the 4-oz mass made an angle of 60° with the radius vector to the center of the filled hole. Where should a 6.0-oz mass now be placed so that the wheel will be in equilibrium in all orientations about its axis? (*Ans:* 4.1 in., 122°)

Fig. 6-11

6-29. Find the center of gravity of the L-shaped area in Fig. 6-12.

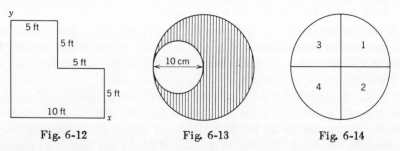

Fig. 6-12   Fig. 6-13   Fig. 6-14

6-30. A disk of uniform density has a hole cut out of it, as shown in Fig. 6-13. Find the center of mass. (*Ans:* 1.67 cm)

6-31. A solid cylinder has a density which varies by quadrants, as shown in Fig. 6-14. When the cylinder is placed on a smooth horizontal plane and allowed to come to equilibrium, what angle will the radius through the point of contact with the plane make with the radius between quadrants of densities 1 and 2? (*Ans:* 153° 30′)

Human levers

6-32. A man weighing 200 lb and carrying a 100-lb bag of cement rises on tiptoes. Calculate the downward force on the astragalus of each foot, and the tension in each Achilles tendon if the dimensions of each foot are those shown in the schematic diagram of Fig. 6-15. (*Ans:* 150 lb, 650 lb)

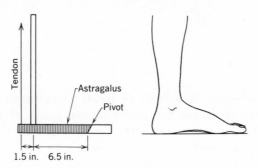

Fig. 6-15

6-33. A man has the dimensions and weights shown in the Fig. 6-16. Keeping his back straight and his arms hanging vertically, how far can he lean over? *Note:* His heels are 6.0 in. from the wall and his weight is on his toes at the maximum point of inclination.

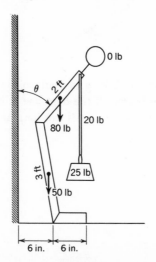

Fig. 6-16

Equilibrium, stable and unstable

6-34. Two weights, W_1 and W_2, are hung at the ends of an L-shaped bar as shown in Fig. 6-17. The bar is pivoted at the point indicated. (a) What is the position of stable equilibrium, and what is the position of unstable equilibrium? (b) Give the value of the angle θ when $W_1 = 1.0$ lb and $W_2 = 2.0$ lb. (*Ans:* Stable for $\theta < \tan^{-1} 2W_1/W_2$; $\theta = 45°$)

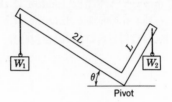

Fig. 6-17

6-35. A car moves in a curve of radius of curvature r. The width between wheels is b, and the height of the center of mass from the ground is h. With what speed must the car move in order that the vertical force on the inside wheels shall be reduced to zero?

6-36. A straight bar of length r is made up of two segments, each of length $r/2$; one segment weighs W lb, the other weighs $2W$ lb. The bar is placed in a smooth spherical bowl of radius r (Fig. 6-18). When the bar comes to rest, what angle α does it make with the horizontal? (*Ans:* 5.5°)

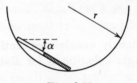

Fig. 6-18

6-37. A uniform bar 8.0 ft long is bent so that a 3.0-ft arm makes an angle of 45° with a 5.0-ft arm. If the bent bar is hooked over a horizontal wire, what angle with the vertical will the long arm make?

CHAPTER 7

Rotational Motion

The average *angular speed* $\overline{\omega}$ of a rotating body is the angle turned per unit time by a line that passes perpendicularly through the axis of rotation:

$$\overline{\omega} = \frac{\theta}{t}. \tag{7-1}$$

Angular distance θ, in radians, is the ratio of the length of arc to its radius. A *radian* is the angle whose intercepted arc is equal to the radius. *Angular acceleration* α, is the rate of change of angular velocity:

$$\overline{\alpha} = \frac{\omega_2 - \omega_1}{t}. \tag{7-2}$$

The equations of uniformly accelerated motion are similar to those for linear motion with angle substituted for distance, angular speed for linear speed, and angular acceleration for linear acceleration.

Table 7-1. Corresponding Equations in Linear and Angular Motion

Quantity	Linear	Angular
Velocity	$\overline{v} = s/t$	$\overline{\omega} = \theta/t$
Acceleration	$\overline{a} = (v_2 - v_1)/t$	$\overline{\alpha} = (\omega_2 - \omega_1)/t$
Uniformly accelerated motion	$v_2 - v_1 = at$	$\omega_2 - \omega_1 = \alpha t$
	$s = v_1 t + \frac{1}{2} at^2$	$\theta = \omega_1 t + \frac{1}{2} at^2$
	$v_2^2 - v_1^2 = 2as$	$\omega_2^2 - \omega_1^2 = 2\alpha\theta$
Newton's second law	$F = ma$	$L = I\alpha$
Work	$\text{Work} = Fs$	$\text{Work} = L\theta$
Power	$P = Fv$	$P = L\omega$
Kinetic energy	$KE = \frac{1}{2} mv^2$	$KE = \frac{1}{2} I\omega^2$
Momentum	$Ft = mv_2 - mv_1$	$Lt = I\omega_2 - I\omega_1$

The *moment of inertia, I* (rotational inertia) for a body about a given axis is the sum of the products of the mass and the square of the radius of each particle of the body:

$$I = \Sigma \; mr^2 \qquad (7\text{-}3)$$

The *radius of gyration k* of a body about an axis is the distance from that axis at which all the mass might be concentrated without altering the moment of inertia. It is defined by

$$I = mk^2 \qquad (7\text{-}4)$$

Table 7-2. Moments of Inertia

Body	Axis	Moment of inertia
Thin ring, radius r	perpendicular axis through center:	mr^2
	along any diameter:	$\frac{1}{2} mr^2$
Circular disk, radius r	perpendicular axis through center:	$\frac{1}{2} mr^2$
	along any diameter:	$\frac{1}{4} mr^2$
Circular cylinder	axis of cylinder:	$\frac{1}{2} mr^2$
	transverse axis through center:	$\frac{1}{4} m\left(r^2 + \frac{1}{3} l^2\right)$
Solid sphere, radius r......	axis through center:	$\frac{2}{5} mr^2$
Thin spherical shell........	axis through center:	$\frac{2}{3} mr^2$
Rod	transverse axis through center:	$\frac{1}{12} ml^2$
	transverse axis at one end:	$\frac{1}{3} ml^2$

For angular motion, *Newton's laws* may be stated:

1. A body does not change its angular velocity unless acted upon by an external, unbalanced force.
2. An unbalanced torque about any axis produces an angular acceleration about that axis, an acceleration which is directly proportional to the torque and inversely proportional to the moment of inertia of the body about that axis.
3. For every torque applied to a body, there is a torque equal in magnitude but opposite in sense applied to another body.

The *work* done by a torque L in turning through an angle θ is

$$\text{work} = L\theta. \qquad (7\text{-}5)$$

The *power* supplied by a torque L is

$$P = L\omega. \qquad (7\text{-}6)$$

Kinetic energy of rotation is given by the equation

$$KE = \frac{1}{2} I \omega^2. \tag{7-7}$$

For a rolling body, the total kinetic energy, including translational and rotational, is

$$KE = \frac{1}{2} m v^2 + \frac{1}{2} I \omega^2. \tag{7-8}$$

Note that in Eqs. (7-5) to (7-8), the angles must be expressed in radian measure.

When a torque is applied to change the spin axis of a spinning body (gyroscope), the axis *precesses* (Fig. 7-1). The angular velocity of

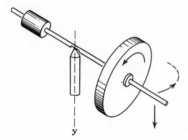

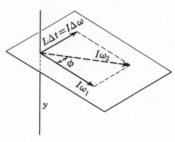

Fig. 7-1. Torque due to gravity causes rotating disk to precess.

Fig. 7-2. Vector diagram for precession.

precession equals the torque producing it divided by the spin angular momentum:

$$\text{angular velocity of precession} = \Omega = \frac{d\phi}{dt} = \frac{L}{I\omega}. \tag{7-9}$$

The direction of precession is at right angles to both the spin and the torque axes; the spin axis rotates toward the torque axis. Precession is a consequence of conservation of angular momentum; in the vector diagram of Fig. 7-2, $L \Delta t = I(\omega_2 - \omega_1) = I \Delta \omega$.

Example: Find the moment of inertia of a uniform flywheel about a perpendicular axis through its center (Fig. 7-3).

Consider a cylindrical shell of radius r, width dr, and thickness l. If the density of the material is ρ, the mass of the shaded element is

$$dm = 2\pi r l \, dr \, \rho,$$

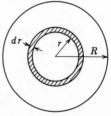

and $\quad I = \int r^2 \, dm = \int_0^R 2\pi l \rho r^3 \, dr = \frac{\pi}{2} \rho l R^4.$

Fig. 7-3

But $\pi R^2 l \rho = m =$ the mass of the disk, so moment of
inertia $l = (1/2)mR^2$. (See Table 7-2).

Example: A 2.0-lb solid cylinder has a radius of 6.0 in. It rests at the
top of an incline 6.0 ft high and 13 ft long (Fig. 7-4). The cylinder is released and rolls down the incline. Find its linear and angular speeds at
the bottom. Assume neglibible energy loss due to friction.

The potential energy of the cylinder at the top of the incline is converted into kinetic energy of translation and rotation as the cylinder rolls
down. At the bottom of the incline the potential energy has been completely converted into kinetic energy: PE = KE.

$$Wh = \tfrac{1}{2}mv^2 + \tfrac{1}{2}I\omega^2,$$

but

$$\omega = v/R \text{ and } I = \tfrac{1}{2}mR^2.$$

Hence

$$Wh = \tfrac{1}{2}mv^2 + 1/2\left(\tfrac{1}{2}mR^2\right)\frac{v^2}{R} = \tfrac{3}{4}mv^2,$$

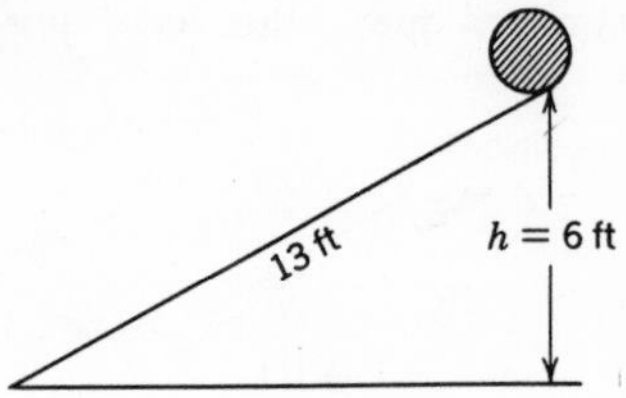

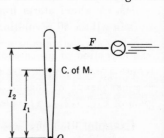

Fig. 7-4

$$Wh = mgh = \tfrac{3}{4}mv^2,$$

$$v = \sqrt{\tfrac{4}{3}gh} = \sqrt{\tfrac{4}{3}(32 \text{ ft/sec}^2)(6.0 \text{ ft})} = 16 \text{ ft/sec},$$

$$\omega = \frac{v}{R} = \frac{16 \text{ ft/sec}}{0.50 \text{ ft}} = 32 \text{ rad/sec}.$$

Note that the linear speed does not depend on the size or the weight of
the cylinder.

Example: Find the point (center of per-
cussion) where a baseball can impart an
impulse Ft to the bat without causing the
hand holding the bat at O to feel any "sting."

The required condition is that the bat
start rotating about O when the blow is
struck.

Linear momentum acquired by the bat:
$m\bar{v} = Ft$.

Angular momentum about axis through
$O: I\omega = Fl_2t$.

But $\bar{v} = \omega l_1$, so

$$l_2 = \frac{I\omega}{m\bar{v}} = \frac{I}{ml_1}.$$

Fig. 7-5

Example: A disk rotating at a speed of 2700 rev/min is supported at one end of its axle (Fig. 7-6). The support is 3.0 in. from the center of gravity, the weight of disk and axle is 4.0 lb, and the moment of inertia is 0.0040 slug-ft². What is the rate of precession?

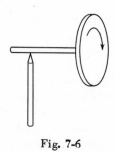

The weight, considered as acting at the center of gravity, produces a torque

Fig. 7-6

$$L = Ws = 4.0 \text{ lb} \times 0.25 \text{ ft} = 1.0 \text{ lb-ft},$$

$$\omega = 2700 \text{ rev/min} = 45 \text{ rev/sec} = 90.0 \text{ rad/sec},$$

$$\Omega = \frac{L}{I\omega} = \frac{1.0 \text{ lb-ft}}{(0.0040 \text{ slug-ft}^2)(90.0 \text{ rad/sec})}$$

$$= 0.88 \text{ rad/sec}.$$

PROBLEMS

Angular speed, acceleration

7-1. The extremity of the hour hand of a clock travels 1/18 as fast as the extremity of the minute hand. If the minute hand is 6.0 in. long, how long is the hour hand? (*Ans*: 4.0 in.)

7-2. A wheel whose diameter is one foot starts from rest with an angular acceleration of 6.0 radians per second per second. At the end of 10 sec, what is (a) the total angle turned through? (b) the final angular velocity? (c) the velocity of a point on the circumference?

7-3. A wheel starts from rest and reaches a rotational speed of 100 rev/min within 30 revolutions. Assuming a uniform angular acceleration, calculate (a) the angular acceleration, (b) the time required to reach this speed. (c) If the wheel has a radius of 2 ft, what is the speed of a point on the rim at 100 rev/min? (*Ans*: $\overline{330}\,\pi$ rad/min², 36 sec; 6.6π ft/sec)

Moment of inertia

7-4. Calculate the moment of inertia of a meter stick, which has a mass of 320 gm, about an axis at right angles to the stick and located at the 25-cm mark.

7-5. A 40-gm hoop of 10.0-cm radius is suspended in a vertical plane by a 50-cm length of massless cord. Find the moment of inertia of the hoop with respect to an axis through the point of suspension normal to the plane of the hoop and string. (*Ans*: 1.48×10^4 gm-cm²)

7-6. Derive an expression for the radius a of the hole which must be drilled into a cylinder of radius R such that the moment of inertia will be reduced by n per cent. The hole and cylinder are coaxial.

7-7. A slender úniform rod is suspended from one end (point O). The mass and length of the rod are m and l, respectively. A point particle, also of mass m, is embedded in the rod and is located a distance x from the point O. It is observed that the radius of gyration of the system about an axis through O and perpendicular to the plane of the paper is $l/2$. The moment of inertia of the uniform rod alone, about the axis of rotation, is $(1/3)\,ml^2$. Evaluate the fraction x/l. (Ans: 0.13)

7-8. A solid is bounded by the surfaces $z = x^2 + y^2$ and $z = 6$, with a varying density, $d = 1 + z$. Find its moment of inertia about the z-axis.

Newton's laws for angular motion

7-9. A torque of 0.24 lb-ft is required to rotate a cylindrical grindstone at uniform angular speed. The grindstone weighs 96 lb and has a radius of 2.00 ft. This grindstone is given an angular speed of 100 rev/min, is released, and is allowed to run until it stops. (a) What is its angular momentum at the instant it is released? (b) How long will it run? (Ans: 20π slug ft^2 sec^{-1}; 4.3 min)

7-10. An unbalanced torque of 5.0 lb-ft acts on a wheel, initially at rest, which weighs 352 lb and has a radius of gyration of 2.0 ft. Compute the number of revolutions the wheel makes in 10.0 sec.

7-11. A 320-lb flywheel has a radius of gyration of 2.0 ft. It is given an angular speed of 900 rev/min and released on its axis. It continues to rotate for 5.0 min. Compute the frictional torque, which is assumed to be constant. (Ans: 12.6 lb-ft)

7-12. Find the torque required to stop a flywheel ($I = 4.0 \times 10^4$ gm-cm^2) from a speed of 1800 rev/min in 12.0 sec.

7-13. A grindstone 50 cm in diameter and weighing 10 kg is making 400 rev/min. What force applied tangent to the wheel will slow it to 100 rev/min in 10 sec? (Ans: $0.25\,n$)

7-14. Two solid wheels each 2.0 ft in diameter and weighing 24 lb are keyed to a solid axle 1.0 ft in diameter and weighing 32 lb. A string wrapped around the axle passes over a massless frictionless pulley and down to a block weighing 160 lb. Find the acceleration of the center of mass of the spool. (Ans: $3/31\,g$)

7-15. A pulley has a radius of gyration of 4.0 in., a diameter of 1.0 ft, and weighs 96 lb. If a 64-lb weight is attached to the pulley by a light cord, (a) what will be its acceleration as it falls? (b) what will be its velocity after it has fallen 10 ft? (Ans: 19 ft/sec^2, 20 ft/sec)

7-16. A grindstone in the form of a solid cylinder weighs 80 lb and is 2.0 ft in diameter. What is the minimum force of constant magnitude which can be applied to the end of a crank 9.0 in. long to bring the grindstone up to an angular velocity of 120 rev/min in 5 sec?

7-17. In the arrangement in Fig. 7-7, the wheel and axle have radii of 10 cm and 5 cm, respectively, a combined mass of 100 gm, and the moment of inertia about the center of the axle is 5000 gm-cm². The mass of the pulley and the mass of the hanging block are each 100 gm. Find the acceleration of the hanging block. (The wheel rolls on the plane without slipping.) (Ans: $\frac{2}{15}g$)

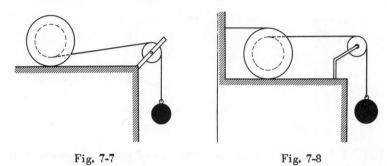

Fig. 7-7   Fig. 7-8

7-18. A spool consists of two solid disks, each of mass 100 gm and radius 12.0 cm, and a solid axle of mass 100 gm and radius 8.0 cm (Fig. 7-8). The spool rests on a perfectly smooth surface. Cords wrapped around the outer rims of the spool run horizontally back to a wall, where they are tied. A cord around the axle passes horizontally out over a massless pulley and down to a body weighing 100 gm. When the system is released, (a) what is the linear acceleration of the center of the spool? (b) In which direction does the spool revolve? (Ans: 75.4 cm/sec²; counterclockwise)

7-19. In the arrangement of Fig. 7-9, the solid disk and the pulley have the same radii, and the disk, pulley, and block all have the same mass. The plane has a slope 30°, and the disk rolls on the incline without slipping. Find the acceleration of the hanging block. (Ans: $\frac{2}{5}g$)

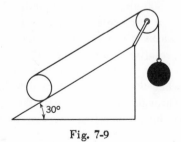

30°

Fig. 7-9

7-20. A boy skating at a speed of 6.0 mi/hr suddenly catches his feet in a crack in the ice. Assuming the boy to be a thin rigid rod of length 3.0 ft, with what speed will the top of his head strike the ice? (Ans: 22 ft/sec)

7-21. A thin rod has a hole fitting onto a threaded screw of pitch P (Fig. 7-10). (The pitch is defined as the linear distance the screw would move per revolution.) The rod has a mass m and a moment of inertia I about the axis of the screw. If the screw stands vertically and is frictionless, what will be the vertical acceleration of the rod, in terms of I, P, and m, and g? (Ans: $mgP^2/4\pi^2 I$)

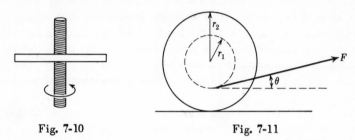

Fig. 7-10   Fig. 7-11

7-22. A hexagonal nut of mass 100 gm and radius of gyration 2.0 cm turns without friction down a vertical screw of 3.0 turns/cm. Starting from rest, how long does it take the nut to run down 10 cm of the screw? (Ans: 5.4 sec)

7-23. A spool of thread with an inner radius r_1 and an outer radius r_2 has a moment of inertia I_0 about the center of mass. The spool is pulled by a thread, as shown in Fig. 7-11, with a constant force F. (a) Find the linear acceleration of the spool if $\theta = 0°$. (b) At what angle θ will the linear acceleration vanish? (Assume that the spool rolls without slipping.) (Ans: $F(r_2^2 - r_1 r_2)/(I + mr_2^2)$; $\cos\theta = r_1/r_2$)

7-24. A small sphere of radius r is placed on top of a large sphere of radius R. If the small sphere just starts to roll from rest at the top point, at what angle will the small sphere leave the large sphere? The sphere rolls without slipping.

7-25. A 160-lb man stands at the rim of a turntable of radius 10.0 ft and moment of inertia 2500 slug-ft². The turntable is mounted on a vertical frictionless shaft at its center. The whole system is initially at rest. The man now walks along the outer edge of the turntable with a velocity of 2.0 ft/sec, relative to the earth. (a) With what angular velocity and in what direction does the turntable rotate? (b) Through what angle will it have rotated when the man has returned to his initial position on the turntable? (c) Through what angle will the turntable have rotated when he reaches his initial position relative to the earth? (Ans: 0.2 rad/sec)

Inclines

7-26. A bowling ball rolling without slipping on a level floor with a speed of 10.0 ft/sec arrives at the foot of an incline which rises 6.0 ft for every 10.0 ft of incline. How far does it roll up the incline before stopping? (*Hint*: Use energy relations.)

7-27. A 30-lb solid sphere 6.0 in. in diameter is at the top of an incline 7.0 ft high and 13 ft long. What linear speed does it acquire in rolling down? (*Ans*: 18 ft/sec)

7-28. A boy standing beside a smooth, inclined plane throws one ball straight up in the air at the same time that he starts a ball rolling up the inclined plane. Both balls have the same initial speed. The boy notices that he catches the ball that was thrown upward at the same instant that the ball on the plane comes to a stop before rolling back down the plane. What was the angle of inclination of the plane with the horizontal? (*Ans*: 30°)

7-29. A steel ball rolls on a glass surface inclined at an angle of 30° with the horizontal. If it starts from rest, how far will it go in 1.00 sec? (*Ans*: 175 cm or 5.71 ft)

7-30. A coin of mass 1.02 gm is projected up a 30° incline with an initial velocity of 600 cm/sec. The coefficient of friction (sliding) between inclined plane and coin is 0.115. Calculate the time elapsed before the coin returns to its original position. (*Ans*: 2.27 sec)

7-31. A cylinder of length 20 cm, radius 20 cm, density $10/3 \pi$ gm/cm³, has a longitudinal hole of radius 10 cm bored in such a way that the axis of the hole is 6.0 cm from the axis of the cylinder. If the cylinder is placed in the angle between a smooth wall and a rough floor, as shown in Fig. 7-12, calculate the forces exerted on the cylinder by the wall and the floor. (*Ans:* Wall, 23 newtons, normal to wall; floor, 20 newtons horizontal)

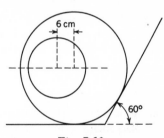

Fig. 7-12

7-32. A solid cylinder of mass m and radius r is rolling down an incline of slope tan θ. What force of friction must exist between the cylinder and the incline so that the cylinder just rolls without slipping? (*Ans*: mg/3 sin θ)

7-33. Two spools having the same mass and dimensions, outer radius $r_2 = 4.0$ in., inner radius $r_1 = 2.0$ in., roll down an incline (Fig. 7-13). A rope has been wrapped around the inner cylinders such that the rope unwinds from the upper spool and winds on the lower one as the spools descend. Due to different mass distributions, the lower and upper spools have different radii of gyration, 2.0 in. and 3.0 in., respectively. (a) Will the rope remain tight? (b) Do the spools have the same acceleration?

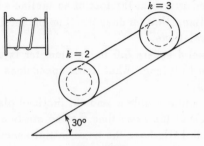

Fig. 7-13

(c) Compute the linear acceleration of the center of the lower spool, using the law of conservation of energy.

7-34. What must be the coefficient of sliding friction between the cylinder and the plane in Fig. 7-14 for the solid cylinder of mass $2m$ not

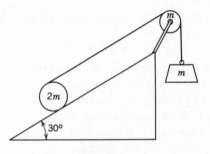

Fig. 7-14

to have any linear motion as the mass m falls? Assume that cylinder $2m$ and pulley m are solid cylinders. (*Ans*: 0.216)

7-35. A truck tire which weighs 30 lb and has an outside diameter of 4.0 ft rolls down an inclined plane with a linear acceleration of 6.0 ft/sec². (a) What is the angular acceleration of the tire about its center? (b) What will be the total kinetic energy of the tire 3.0 sec after it starts from rest? (c) At the bottom of the inclined plane, the total kinetic energy is 3000 ft-lb. What vertical distance did the tire move? (d) At what angle is the plane inclined to the horizontal? (*Ans*: 3.0 rad/sec²; 500 ft-lb; 100 ft; 7.2°)

7-36. By applying the conservation of energy principle, show that the speed of an object that slides down a plane of height h (neglecting friction) is $\sqrt{2}$ times greater than the speed of a hoop which rolls down the incline.

Energy

7-37. Compute the angular speed of a flywheel which weighs 352 lb, has a radius of gyration of 2.00 ft, and a kinetic energy of 8000 ft-lb. (*Ans:* 19.1 rad/sec)

7-38. A grindstone 3.0 ft in diameter weighs 200 lb. Determine its kinetic energy when rotating at 100 rev/min. (*Ans:* 390 ft-lb)

7-39. A 40-kg flywheel has a radius of gyration of 0.50 m. What is its angular speed when its rotational kinetic energy is equal to the translational kinetic energy of 2.0-kg projectile moving with a speed of 400 m/sec? (*Ans:* 180 rad/sec)

7-40. The wheel in Fig. 7-15 has an outside radius of 0.50 m, a radius of gyration of 0.30 m, and a mass of 2.0 kg. The 5.0-kg mass is released, and the 3.0-kg mass is raised, the wheel being turned by the cord, without slipping. Using the conservation of energy principle, find the

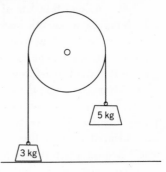

Fig. 7-15

speed with which the 5-kg mass strikes the floor. (Make sure that you take all of energy terms into account.)

7-41. A 400-lb turntable which can be thought of as a solid disk of 10-ft radius is rotating freely about an axis through its center at an angular·speed of 1.0 rad/sec. A 200-lb man is standing at the edge of the turntable. The man walks radially inward to a position 5.0 ft from the center. (a) What is the angular speed of the turntable when the man is in this position? (b) Is the change in kinetic energy of the system an increase or a decrease? (c) What is responsible for this change? (*Ans:* 1.6 rad/sec)

Power

7-42. The drive shaft of an automobile rotates at an angular speed of 3600 rev/min and transmits 120 hp to the rear wheels. Compute the torque developed by the engine.

7-43. Compute the torque developed by an airplane engine whose output is 2000 hp at an angular velocity of 2400 rev/min. (b) If a drum 18 in. in diameter were attached to the engine shaft, and the power output of the engine were used to raise a weight hanging from a rope wrapped around the shaft, how large a weight could be lifted? (c) With what velocity would it rise? (*Ans:* 440 lb-ft; 580 lb; 140 ft/sec)

7-44. The drive shaft of an automobile rotates at an angular speed of 3600 rev/min and transmits 120 hp to the rear wheels. Compute the torque developed by the engine. (1 hp = 550 ft-lb/sec.)

Momentum, impulse

7-45. A uniform plank originally standing upright falls to earth, pivoting around its bottom end. It is slightly bowed, so that only its ends strike the ground (Fig. 7-16). What is the ratio of the impulses delivered to the ground by each end as the plank falls?

Fig. 7-16

7-46. A long thin bar of mass m and length l is lying on a smooth horizontal table. It is struck at one end at right angles to the bar with a horizontal impulse of Ft. When the bar has first turned end-for-end, how far is it displaced from its original position? (*Ans:* $\pi l/6$)

7-47. A uniform rod of length l rotates without friction in a horizontal plane about a fixed vertical axis through the center. Two small bodies are mounted so that they can slide without friction along the rod. The small bodies are initially held by catches at positions x (less than $l/2$) on either side of the center of the rod. The entire system is initially rotating at ω_i rad/sec. Without otherwise changing the system, the catches are released and the masses slide along the rod and fly off the ends. Let ω_f be the angular velocity of the rod after the small masses leave it. Is ω_f greater than, equal to, or less than ω_i? Give a reason for your answer, stating what principle or principles you used in arriving at your conclusion.

7-48. Two spheres are mounted on a rotating horizontal bar as in Fig. 7-17. Provision is made to bring the spheres closer together without applying any external torque to the system. While rotating at 20

Fig. 7-17

rad/sec in a path radius of 40 cm, the spheres are quickly pulled together so that they rotate at a radius of 10 cm. The spheres each have a radius of 2.0 cm and a mass of 200 gm. Neglect the mass of the supporting bar. (a) What is the new angular velocity? (b) Calculate the kinetic energies in the initial (40-cm radius) and final (10-cm radius) paths. (c) Discuss the result in part (b) in terms of energy conservation.

7-49. A 160-lb man stands on the edge of a turntable of radius 5.0 ft and moment of inertia 75 slug-ft^2. He fires a gun along a tangent of the turntable. The bullet has a mass of 0.0020 slug and leaves the gun with a muzzle speed of 2000 ft/sec. (a) Find the impulse of the force acting on the man. (b) Find the angular impulse. (c) Find the angular velocity of the turntable after the gun was fired. (*Ans*: 4.0 slug-ft/sec, 20 slug-ft²/sec, 0.10 rad/sec)

Precession, gyroscope

7-50. A single-engine light plane has a propeller of large rotational inertia. The propeller turns counterclockwise as viewed from the cockpit. Suppose the pilot makes a right turn; state what effect, if any, the gyroscopic action of the propeller will have on the plane.

7-51. The disk of Fig. 7-18 has a radius of 3.0 in. and weighs 10 lb. How fast must it rotate and in what direction so that it will precess counterclockwise (when viewed from above) at a rate of 5.0 rad/sec? Distance $l_1 = 6.0$ in. (*Ans:* 16 rev/sec)

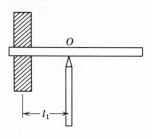

Fig. 7-18

7-52. A 160-lb disk of radius 2.0 ft rotates with a speed of 40 rad/sec. The distance l_1 from its center to the support is 2.0 ft. Find the angular speed of precession, and its direction, if the top of the disk is rotating "out."

7-53. A 320-lb disk of radius 2.0 ft rotates at the rate 10 rad/sec in a plane 1.0 ft from the point at which its axle is supported ($l_1 = 1.0$ ft). At what distance from O should a 10-lb weight be hung from the axle in order to cause a counterclockwise precession of 0.25 rad/sec, when viewed from above? A 128-lb weight is already hung from the axle at a distance 4.0 ft from O. (*Ans:* 14 or 24 ft, depending on direction of rotation)

7-54. Describe the action of a bicycle wheel, in terms of precessional motion, when, while traveling in a straight line, the rider suddenly begins to lean (tilt) toward the right. Use vector diagrams.

7-55. A gyroscope consists of a disk of radius 2.0 cm mounted as shown in Fig. 7-19, with its center of mass a distance of 2.0 cm from the point of support P, on a thin axis of length l. The disk is rotating in a counterclockwise direction (looking from A) around this axis at 100 rev/sec. If it is simultaneously being forced to precess with an angular velocity of

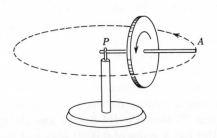

Fig. 7-19

2.0 rev/sec, without nutation, in a horizontal plane around P by a force applied at A, what is the magnitude and direction of this force at A? The mass of the disk is 2.0 gm. Neglect friction and the mass of the axial rod. $(Ans:\ \dfrac{2.8 \times 10^4}{l}\ \text{dynes})$

Center of percussion

7-56. A bar 3.0 ft long (Fig. 7-20) is pivoted at its center, has a moment of inertia 3.0 lb-ft², and is rotating with an angular velocity of 10 rad/sec. When the bar is vertical, it is struck by a ball of 1.0-lb mass, at height l above the axis of rotation, moving horizontally 10 ft/sec. Find the height l and the velocity with which the ball rebounds if the impact is such as to stop rotation of the bar. The coefficient of restitution is 1. $(Ans:$ 1 ft; 20 ft/sec$)$

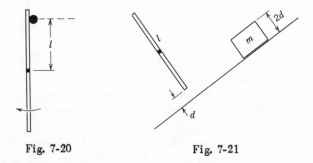

Fig. 7-20   Fig. 7-21

7-57. A thin rectangular sheet of mass 30 lb (Fig. 7-21) is mounted in the middle of a frictionless axle that lies in the plane of the sheet and perpendicular to the long edge. The axle is mounted above and parallel to an inclined frictionless plane so that the short edge of the sheet, in swinging, clears the plane by a distance d. The sheet is swung into a position perpendicular to the plane, and a rectangular block of mass m and height $2\,d$ above the plane slides freely down and hits the sheet. The coefficient of restitution between block and sheet is 1. If it is observed that the block stops momentarily on hitting the sheet, what is the value of m, the mass of the block? $(Ans:$ 10 lb$)$

CHAPTER 8

Elasticity

Vibratory and Simple Harmonic Motion

Elasticity is a property of a body that causes it to resist deformation and to recover after removal of the deforming force.

Tensile stress is the force per unit cross-sectional area. The smallest stress that produces a permanent deformation is called the *elastic limit. Tensile strain* is the increase in length per unit length.

Hooke's law expresses the fact that, within the limits of elasticity, stress is proportional to strain, or the elongation x is proportional to the force F:

$$\frac{F}{A} = Y\,\frac{\Delta x}{x} \quad \text{or} \quad F = kx. \qquad (8\text{-}1)$$

A *modulus of elasticity* is found by dividing the stress by the corresponding strain; *Young's modulus* Y is the ratio of tensile stress to tensile strain:

$$Y = \frac{F/A}{\Delta L/L}. \qquad (8\text{-}2)$$

The *bulk modulus* B or *coefficient of volume elasticity* is the ratio of volume stress to volume strain:

$$B = \frac{F/A}{\Delta V/V}. \qquad (8\text{-}3)$$

Compressibility is the reciprocal of the bulk modulus. The *shear modulus* or *coefficient of rigidity* is the ratio of shearing stress to shearing strain:

$$n = \frac{F/A}{\phi}. \qquad (8\text{-}4)$$

Example: Young's modulus for steel is 20×10^6 lb/in.^{2}. How much force is necessary to stretch a steel rod 1.00 in.^{2} in cross section by 1/100,000 of its original length?

From Eq. (8-2),

$$F = \frac{\Delta l}{l} \, YA = 10^{-5}(20 \times 10^6 \text{ lb/in.}^2)(1.00 \text{ in.}^2) = 200 \text{ lb.}$$

Example: Compute the elongations of the aluminum wire of 0.040-in. diameter $(Y = 10 \times 10^5$ lb/in.$^2)$ and the copper wire of 0.060-in. diameter $(Y = 14 \times 10^6$ lb/in.$^2)$ when loaded as shown in Fig. 8-1.

The load on the aluminum wire is 11.0 lb. From Eq. (8-2),

elongation $= \Delta l = \dfrac{Fl}{YA}$

$= \dfrac{(11.0 \text{ lb})(3.0 \text{ ft})}{10 \times 10 \text{ lb/in.}^2 \, (\pi \, 0.040/4 \text{ in.}^2)} = 0.0026$ in.

The load on the copper wire is 8.0 lb. From Eq. (8-2),

elongation $\Delta l = \dfrac{Fl}{YA} = \dfrac{(8.0 \text{ lb})(2.0 \text{ ft})}{14 \times 10^6 \text{ lb/in.}^2 \, (\pi \, 0.060^2/4 \text{ in.}^2)}$

$= 0.00010$ in.

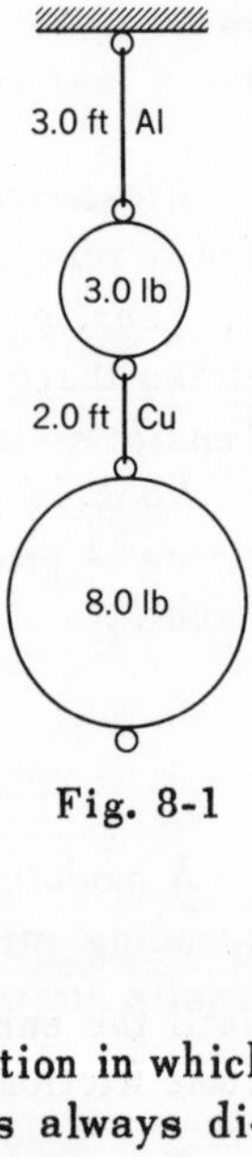

Fig. 8-1

Periodic motion is motion in which the body moves back and forth over a fixed path, returning to each position and velocity after a definite interval of time.

Simple harmonic motion (SHM) is that type of vibratory motion in which the acceleration is proportional to the displacement and is always directed toward the position of equilibrium:

$$a = -kx. \tag{8-5}$$

Simple harmonic motion is always motion along a straight line. Many vibrations that are not strictly simple harmonic are very close approximations and may be treated as such. The motion of the projection on a diameter of a point that moves at constant speed on the "circle of reference" describes simple harmonic motion.

The *period T* of a vibratory motion is the time required for one complete oscillation:

$$T = 2\pi \sqrt{\frac{m}{K}} \tag{8-6}$$

where K is the force constant, the restoring force per unit displacement.

The *frequency* f is the number of complete oscillations per second: $f = 1/T$.

The *amplitude* of the motion is the maximum displacement from the equilibrium position.

A *simple pendulum* is one which consists of a concentrated bob supported by a very light string. Its period is given by

$$T = 2\pi \sqrt{\frac{l}{g}}. \tag{8-7}$$

A *physical pendulum* (or compound pendulum) is a body which oscillates in the manner of a simple pendulum but whose mass is distributed, rather than concentrated. If h is the distance from the support to the center of gravity, the period of a physical pendulum is given by

$$T = 2\pi \sqrt{\frac{I}{mgh}}. \tag{8-8}$$

A *torsion pendulum* vibrates with *simple angular harmonic motion.* Its period is given by

$$T = 2\pi \sqrt{\frac{I}{K_0}}, \tag{8-9}$$

where K_0, the *moment of torsion,* is the ratio of the torque to the angle of twist produced by that torque. It depends on the length, diameter, and material of the rod.

Resonance occurs when a periodic driving force is impressed upon a system whose natural frequency of vibration is the same as that of the driving force. When this happens, the amplitude of vibration builds up until the energy supplied by the driving force is just sufficient to overcome friction in the system.

Example: A 4.0-lb body vibrates along x',x (Fig. 8-2) in simple harmonic motion with an amplitude of 3.0 in. and a period of 5.0 sec. Find the acceleration and the speed (a) at the mid-point, (b) at the end of the path, and (c) at a point 2.0 in. from the mid-point.

Since the amplitude is 3.0 in., the radius of the reference circle is 3.0 in. The speed of the particle in the reference circle is

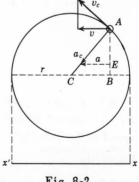

Fig. 8-2

$$v_c = \frac{2\pi r}{T} = \frac{2\pi(3.0 \text{ in.})}{5.0 \text{ sec}} = 3.8 \text{ in./sec.}$$

At the mid-point of the path, the velocity in the reference circle is the same as that of the vibrating body:

$$v_1 = v_c = 3.8 \text{ in./sec} = 0.32 \text{ ft/sec.}$$

At the mid-point, the acceleration in the reference circle is perpendicular to the diameter, and hence the component parallel to the path of the vibrating body is zero:

$$a_1 = 0.$$

At the end point, the velocity in the reference circle is perpendicular to the path of vibration, and hence has no component in that direction:

$$v_2 = 0.$$

At the end point, the acceleration in the reference circle is the same as the acceleration in the vibration:

$$a_2 = a_c = \frac{v_c^2}{r} = \frac{(3.8 \text{ in./sec})^2}{3.0 \text{ in.}} = 4.8 \text{ in./sec}^2 = 0.40 \text{ ft/sec}^2.$$

At the point 2.0 in. from the mid-point, we can find the acceleration by use of

$$\frac{a}{a_c} = \frac{-x}{r}; \ a = \frac{-a_c x}{r} = \frac{-(4.8 \text{ in./sec}^2)(2.0 \text{ in.})}{3.0 \text{ in.}}$$

$$= -3.2 \text{ in./sec}^2 = -0.27 \text{ ft/sec}^2.$$

From the Fig. 8-2, the velocity in the path of vibration is the component v of the velocity v_c in the reference circle. The geometry of the figure gives the following:

$$v = v_c \cos BAC = v_c \frac{BA}{CA}; \quad CA = r = 3.0 \text{ in.,}$$

$$BA = \sqrt{r^2 - x^2} = \sqrt{(3.0 \text{ in.})^2 - (2.0 \text{ in.})^2} = 2.2 \text{ in.,}$$

$$v = (3.8 \text{ in./sec}) \frac{2.2 \text{ in.}}{3.0 \text{ in.}} = 2.8 \text{ in./sec} = 0.23 \text{ ft/sec.}$$

PROBLEMS

8-1. A body has SHM of amplitude 20 cm. Its average speed between the mid-point of its path and the end is 100 cm/sec. What is the maximum speed of the body?

Elasticity

8-2. What is meant by (a) a perfectly elastic material? (b) a perfectly inelastic material?

8-3. A stiff spring (one which requires a large force to stretch it unit distance) and a weak spring, each with one end fixed, are stretched until the applied force is the same in each case. On which spring was the greater work done? Explain.

8-4. A vertical spring is 10 cm long when supporting a load of 20 kg, and 12 cm long for a load of 32 kg. How many joules of work are required to stretch the spring from 10 to 15 cm? (*Ans:* 17 joules)

8-5. In testing the elastic properties of steel balls they are dropped upon a steel plate having elastic properties as nearly as possible equal to those of the balls. A steel ball is dropped from a height of 40 cm and rebounds to a height of 36 cm. (a) What is the coefficient of restitution? (b) To what height will the ball rebound on its second trip? (*Ans:* 0.95, $h_2 = 32$ cm)

8-6. A spring which is 12 cm long uncompressed is standing upright on the ground. The spring is weightless. A ball which weighs 100 dynes falls on the spring and compresses it 2.0 cm. If the spring constant is 300 dynes/cm, find the maximum height from the ground to which the ball will rise. Neglect air resistance. (*Ans:* 24 cm)

8-7. If T is the stress and N is the strain in the block of Fig. 8-3, derive the following relation: Elastic potential energy $= \frac{1}{2} TN$.

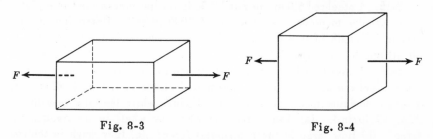

Fig. 8-3   Fig. 8-4

8-8. A cube is held in tension by the forces shown in Fig. 8-4. Show that the fractional decrease in the area perpendicular to the forces is given by $2\sigma\varepsilon$, where ε is the strain of the cube.

Breaking stress

8-9. If the breaking stress of steel is 4.0×10^{10} dynes/cm², what is the critical rim velocity of a steel tire rotating about its axis of symmetry? (*Ans:* 7.2×10^4 cm/sec)

8-10. The breaking load for copper wire is about 4.00×10^6 gm/cm²; its density is 8.9 gm/cm³. If a copper wire were suspended vertically from one end, how long would it have to be to break because of its own weight? (*Ans:* $44\overline{9}0$ m)

8-11. A flat 20-ft by 30-ft roof containing 75 ft³ of pine lumber and 500 lb of roofing material was recently loaded with snow. When the snow reached an average depth of 30 in., a vertical pine post 2 by 4 in., presumably supporting 1/12 of the roof and its load, snapped. The specific gravity of snow is 0.10; the specific gravity of pine is 0.60; and Young's modulus for pine is 1.4×10^6 lb/in.^{2}. Find (a) the breaking stress of the post, (b) the breaking strain of the post.

Young's modulus

8-12. A wire 1000 in. long and 0.010 in.^{2} in cross-sectional area is stretched 4.00 in. by a force of 2000 lb. (a) What is the stress? (b) What is the strain? (c) What is Young's modulus for the wire? (*Ans:* 2.00×10^5 lb/in.^{2}; 4.00×10^{-3}; 5.0×10^7 lb/in.^{2})

8-13. A vertical copper wire 160 cm long with a cross-sectional of 0.12 mm^2 is loaded at the lower end with 3000 gm. The upper end is fixed. Young's modulus for copper is 12×10^{11} dynes/cm^2. Find the stress, the strain, and the elongation. (*Ans:* 2.45×10^9 dynes/cm^2; 0.002; 3.3 mm)

8-14. If a steel wire 10 ft long is to support a 600-lb load with an elongation of no more than 1/8 in., (a) what must be the cross-sectional area of the wire? (b) If a copper wire is used instead of the steel, how must its diameter be related to that of the steel wire? Young's modulus: steel, 30×10^6 lb/in.^{2}; copper, 15×10^6 lb/in.^{2}. (*Ans:* 0.019 in.^{2}; $d_{Cu} = 4d_{Fe}$)

8-15. A steel rod 6.0 in. long and 0.50 in. in diameter is used as a piston in a cylinder to produce a pressure of 2000 lb/in.^{2}. Determine the decrease in length of this rod, assuming that Young's modulus for steel is 30 million lb/in.^{2}. (*Ans:* 0.00040 in.)

8-16. A 3.0-lb body is rotating in a horizontal circle at the end of a 2.0-ft steel rod at a rate of 600 rev/min. The rod is 1/4 in. in diameter. Young's modulus for steel is 30×10^6 lb/in.^{2}, while the bulk modulus is 27×10^6 lb/in.^{2}. (a) What force (on what, by what) is the centripetal force? (b) How large is the centripetal force? (c) How much is the rod stretched by the forces acting on it? (Neglect the mass of the rod.) (*Ans:* 12 lb; 0.0077 in.)

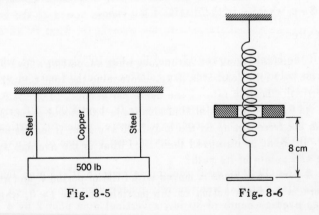

Fig. 8-5   Fig. 8-6

8-17. Two steel wires, each of diameter 1.0 mm and length 100.5 cm, and a copper wire of the same diameter but of length 100.0 cm, are attached to a 500-lb weight and then hung as shown in Fig. 8-5, with symmetrical suspension. What is the final length of the wires? (*Ans:* 101.0 cm)

8-18. A massless helical spring of unstretched length 9.0 cm is stretched 1.0 cm by a 100-gm hanger attached to its lower end (Fig. 8-6). A 100-gm block is dropped on the hanger from a height of 8 cm above it. If this second mass remains on the hanger, to what maximum length will the spring be stretched by the impact? Assume that Hooke's law holds throughout the extension. (*Ans:* 14 cm)

8-19. A steel wire, of cross-sectional area 1.00 mm², unstretched length 100.0 cm, and negligible weight, is attached to two immovable supports 100 cm apart. A weight of 2.55 kg is hung from the mid-point of the wire. Find the distance h through which the mid-point of the wire sags. (Justifiable approximations: $\sin \theta = \tan \theta = \theta$; $\cos \theta = 1 - \theta^2/2$.) (*Ans:* 2.5 cm)

Torsion

8-20. A round steel rod of length 1000 cm and diameter 1.0 cm is fastened into one end of the hub of a wheel of radius 100 cm. A round aluminum rod of length 500 cm and diameter 2.0 cm is fastened into the other end of the hub, the two rods being coaxial with the axis of the wheel. The outer ends of the rods are immovably clamped. What is the angular deflection of the wheel when a 2.0-kg block is hung on a cord around its rim? (*Ans:* 10.3°)

Simple harmonic motion

8-21. SHM is defined by various textbooks as (a) motion in which $a = -cx$, (b) motion in which $x = r \sin \omega t$ (or $x = r \cos \omega t$), and (c) the projection on a diameter of a point moving with uniform circular motion. Show that these three statements are equivalent.

8-22. A body of mass 200 gm has SHM of amplitude 12 cm and frequency 10 cycles/sec. (a) What is the average speed of the body in a passage from one end of its path to the other? (b) What is its maximum acceleration?

8-23. A vertical spring is 60.0 cm long when supporting a load of 20.0 kg and 70.0 cm long for a load of 30.0 kg. Determine the load required to produce a vertical vibration rate of one cycle per second. (*Ans:* 24.8 kg)

8-24. An 8.0-lb body has SHM of amplitude 1.00 ft and period 3.00 sec. (a) What is the force acting on the body 5.25 sec after it leaves one end of the path? (b) What is its speed then? (c) What is the average speed between the end points of its path?

8-25. A particle of mass m moves with SHM of period T and amplitude A. If there is no force acting on the particle at time $t = 0$, what is the force at $t = T/6$?

8-26. A 16-lb force stretches a certain spring one foot. A 32-lb load is put on the spring and it is pulled down 6.0 in. below the equilibrium position and released. Find the period of the SHM. (Leave answer in terms of π.)

8-27. A ping-pong ball is made to move in a horizontal circle of 5.0-cm radius. The shadow of the ball cast by parallel light on the wall performs motion like SHM. The ball makes 4.0 rev/sec. Leaving your answers in terms of π: (a) What is the period of motion of the shadow? (b) What is the maximum displacement of the shadow? The minimum displacement? (c) What is the maximum velocity of the shadow? The minimum velocity? (d) What is the maximum acceleration of the shadow? The minimum? (e) For the shadow, the maximum acceleration occurs when the velocity is a .... and the displacement is a ....

8-28. A 20-gm hanger with a 5.0-gm weight in it is hung from a vertical spring. When the spring is displaced from equilibrium the system is found to vibrate in vertical SHM with a period of $\pi/3$ sec. If the 5-gm weight is replaced by a 25-gm weight, how far can the spring be displaced from equilibrium before release if the weight is not to jump out of the weight hanger? (*Ans:* 49 cm)

8-29. A vertical spring which obeys Hooke's law is extended 0.40 cm by the weight of a 300-gm load. Then a 500-gm block is added and the system is released. (a) What is the maximum extension produced, measured from the original position of the unloaded spring? (b) What is the total potential energy acquired by the spring when it comes to equilibrium? (c) What is the frequency of oscillation of the spring? (d) What is the amplitude?

8-30. A platform is executing SHM in a vertical direction, with amplitude $A = 0.096$ in. Find the frequency at which a block resting on this platform would just lose contact with the platform at some instant of the cycle.

8-31. Two identical rollers are mounted in a horizontal plane with their axes parallel, a distance $2d$ apart. The two rollers are rotating inwardly at the top with the same angular velocity ω, and a long uniform board is laid across them in a direction perpendicular to their axes. If the board is not originally placed so that its center of gravity lies midway between the rollers, (a) prove that the board will oscillate lengthwise in SHM, and (b) find the period of such oscillation. The coefficient of sliding friction between the roller and board is μ. (*Ans:* $2\pi\sqrt{d/\mu g}$)

8-32. A disk of mass m and radius r is pivoted to rotate freely about an axis through its center. Two springs of force constant k are hung from the ceiling and are attached by strings to the rim of the disk. If the disk is displaced from equilibrium position, find the period of the resulting oscillations. (Assume both strings taut at all times; assume the displacements $\theta \ll 1$ radian.)

8-33. A wire of length $4l$ and total mass m is bent into a square and suspended from one corner by a frictionless peg. Find the period for small oscillations of the square, oscillating in its own plane. (*Ans:* $2\pi\sqrt{5\sqrt{2}\,l/6g}$)

Pendulum

8-34. Calculate the length of a pendulum which is designed to have a frequency of vibration of 60 cycles/min.

8-35. A clock has a pendulum which "beats seconds" (the period is two seconds) in Ithaca, where $g = 980.300$ cm/sec². How many seconds will this clock gain or lose in a day if it is taken to San Francisco, where $g = 979.965$ cm/sec²? (*Ans:* Loses 14.4 sec/day)

8-36. A pendulum bob on a 40-ft wire, in an unused elevator shaft, is carefully set into oscillation in a plane. During one day, what observations can be made on the motion of the pendulum which give evidence that the earth is rotating about its axis?

8-37. Given a pendulum of period T. What will its period be if the mass and length are both doubled?

8-38. Is the tension in the cord of a simple pendulum less than, equal to, or greater than, the weight of the bob when the bob passes through the lowest point of its path? Explain.

8-39. At a certain place a simple pendulum 100 cm long makes 250 complete vibrations in 8.35 min. Determine "g." (*Ans:* 32.27 ft/sec²)

8-40. (a) If the equivalent length of a clock pendulum increases by 0.01% because of thermal expansion, would the clock run "slow" or "fast," and by how many seconds per day? (b) What force would be needed in the absence of a temperature change to cause an equal increase in length if Young's modulus for the pendulum is 10^{12} dynes/cm² and the cross-sectional area is 1.00 cm²?

8-41. A rocket carrying a pendulum clock has a motor that delivers a thrust five times the total weight of the rocket. The rocket is fired at time $t = 0$ and rises vertically. After 5 sec its fuel is exhausted. Find the time by the pendulum clock when a clock on the ground reads $t = 15$ sec. (Neglect change in g with altitude.)

8-42. A pendulum consists of a 1.0-lb weight attached to a string of length l. The string has a breaking strength of 1.0 lb. If the pendulum is released from a horizontal position, what angle does it make with the vertical when the string breaks?

8-43. A slender homogeneous rod of mass m and length l is hinged at one end and supported in a horizontal position by a vertical spring attached to it at a distance d from the hinged end. If the free end of the rod is given a small vertical displacement, and is released, calculate the period of the ensuing oscillations if the force constant of the spring is k. (*Ans:* $2\pi(l/a)\sqrt{m/3k}$)

8-44. A small ball rolls in a horizontal orbit around the inside of a hollow circular cone of half angle ϕ whose axis stands vertical. Given that the plane of the orbit is at a distance h above the apex of the cone, calculate the length of the equivalent ideal pendulum. (*Ans:* $h \tan^2 \phi$)

8-45. A uniform cylinder of radius r rolls without slipping in a cylindrical trough of greater radius r', under the influence of gravity. (a) Show that the motion of the axis of the cylinder is simple vibratory for small amplitudes. (b) Find the period of a complete oscillation. (*Ans:* $2\pi\sqrt{3(r'-r)/2g}$)

CHAPTER 9

·

Mechanics of Fluids

The *density* ρ of a substance is its mass per unit volume:

$$\rho = \frac{m}{V}. \qquad (9\text{-}1)$$

Weight-density is weight per unit volume:

$$D = \frac{W}{V}. \qquad (9\text{-}2)$$

The *specific gravity* of a substance is the ratio of its density to the density of water.

Archimedes' principle states that a body wholly or partly submerged in a fluid is buoyed up by a force equal to the weight of the fluid displaced.

Example: A piece of metal of density 7.80 gm/cm³ weighs 429 gm when immersed completely in nitrobenzene of density 1.20 gm/cm³. What is the volume of the metal?

By Archimedes' principle,

$$429 \text{ gm} = V\,(7.80 - 1.20) \text{ gm/cm}^3,$$

$$V = \frac{429 \text{ gm}}{6.60 \text{ gm/cm}^3} = 65 \text{ cm}^3.$$

Pressure p is force per unit area:

$$p = \frac{F}{A}. \qquad (9\text{-}3)$$

At a depth h below the free surface, the pressure due to a liquid of weight-density D is

$$p = hD = h\rho g. \qquad (9\text{-}4)$$

Example: Find the pressure due to a column of mercury 76 cm high.

$$p = h\rho g = (76.0 \text{ cm}) (13.6 \text{ gm/cm}^3) (980 \text{ cm/sec}^2)$$

$$= 1,01\overline{3},000 \text{ dynes/cm}^2.$$

It is convenient to remember that a pressure of 1 standard atmosphere (76 cm of mercury) is nearly equal to 1 million dynes/cm².

Example: A dam is filled with water to a depth of 10.0 ft (Fig. 9-1). Compute for a 1.0 length of the dam the force on it.

Consider the force on a strip of width ds and length l at right angles to the plane of the page:

$$dF = \rho g y l \, ds.$$

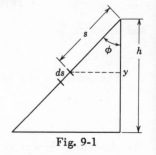

But $s = y/\cos \phi$, so $dF = \dfrac{\rho g l}{\cos \phi} y \, dy,$

$$F = \frac{\rho g l}{\cos \phi} \int_0^h y \, dy = \frac{\rho g l}{\cos \phi} \frac{h^2}{2}.$$

Fig. 9-1

But $\rho g h$ is the pressure, p_b, at the bottom; $hl/\cos \phi = A$, the area of the dam, hence the force on the dam is

$$F = \tfrac{1}{2} p_b A.$$

In this case, the force F_1 on a 1.0-ft length of dam equals

$$(62.4 \text{ lb/ft}^3) \tfrac{1}{2} (10 \text{ ft}) (1.0 \text{ ft}) = 3\overline{1}0 \text{ lb}.$$

Pascal's law states that an external pressure applied to a confined liquid increases the pressure at every point in the liquid by an amount equal to the external pressure.

A barometer is an instrument for measuring air pressure, in terms of the height h, Eq. (9-4), of a column of mercury which produces the same pressure at its base.

The rate of flow R of a fluid through a pipe is usually measured as the volume that passes a certain cross section per unit time.

$$\text{Flow rate} = \text{area} \times \text{speed} \quad \text{or} \quad R = Av. \tag{9-5}$$

In the steady, streamline flow of a fluid, the motion of its molecules is orderly, all molecules which pass a given point in the flow proceed with the same velocity, and the motion is predictable at all points. In turbulent flow, a churning takes place, eddies are formed, and the motion of the molecules is unpredictable in detail.

In the steady flow of a liquid the pressure is least where the velocity is greatest. By Bernoulli's theorem, the sum of the pressure head, the elevation head, and the velocity head remains constant:

$$\frac{p_1}{\rho g} + h_1 + \frac{v_1^2}{2g} = \text{constant}. \qquad (9\text{-}6)$$

Bernoulli's principle is applied in a Venturi flow meter (Fig. 9-2) to measure the rate of flow of a fluid:

$$v = a \sqrt{\frac{2 \rho g h}{\rho (A^2 - a^2)}}, \qquad (9\text{-}7)$$

and from Eq. (9-5),

$$R = a \sqrt{\frac{2 g \rho}{\rho} h}.$$

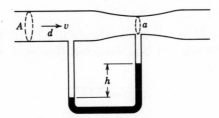

Fig. 9-2. During flow through a constriction, decrease in pressure accompanies increase in speed.

Example: Water flows at the rate of 300 ft³/min through an inclined pipe. At a, where the diameter is 12 in., the pressure is 15 lb/in.². What is the pressure at b, where the diameter is 6.0 in., and the center of the pipe is 2.0 ft lower than at a?

$$A_1 v_1 = A_2 v_2 = \frac{300 \text{ ft}^3/\text{min}}{60 \text{ sec/min}} = 5.0 \text{ ft}^3/\text{sec},$$

$$\frac{A_1}{A_2} = \frac{v_2}{v_1} = \frac{\pi (6.0 \text{ in.})^2}{\pi (3.0 \text{ in.})^2} = 4.0,$$

$$v_1 = \frac{5.0 \text{ ft}^3/\text{sec}}{\pi (\frac{1}{2} \text{ ft})^2} = 6.4 \text{ ft/sec},$$

$$v_2 = 4 v_1 = 26 \text{ ft/sec},$$

$$p_1 = (15 \text{ lb/in.}^2)(144 \text{ in.}^2/\text{ft}^2) = 2\overline{2}00 \text{ lb/ft}^2.$$

For water, $D = 62.4$ lb/ft³, therefore $\rho = 1.94$ slugs/ft³. From Eq. (9-6),

$$\frac{p_1}{\rho g} + h_1 + \frac{v_1^2}{2g} = \frac{p_2}{\rho g} + h_2 + \frac{v_2^2}{2g},$$

$$p_2 = p_1 + \rho g (h_1 - h_2) + \frac{\rho}{2} (v_1^2 - v_2^2)$$

$$= 2\overline{2}00 \text{ lb/ft}^2 + (62.4 \text{ lb/ft}^3)(2.0 \text{ ft}) + \frac{1.94 \text{ slug/ft}^3}{2} (6.4^2 - 26^2)(\text{ft/sec})^2$$

$$= 2\overline{2}00 + 1\overline{2}0 - 6\overline{2}0 \text{ lb/ft}^2 = 1\overline{7}00 \text{ lb/ft}^2 = 12 \text{ lb/in.}^2.$$

An *airfoil* is any surface designed to obtain a reacting force from the air through which it moves.

In a *turbine*, the change in *momentum* of a fluid as it is deflected by the blades causes the shaft to rotate.

The speed with which a liquid escapes from a vessel through an orifice is given by *Torricelli's theorem:*

$$v = \sqrt{2gh}. \tag{9-8}$$

Example: A tank 30 ft tall is completely filled with water. Halfway up, there is a circular hole of 1.0-in. diameter. How much water will squirt out of this hole per hour?

$$v = \sqrt{2gh} = \sqrt{2 \times 32 \text{ ft/sec}^2 \ 15 \text{ ft}} = 31.9 \text{ ft/sec},$$

$$\text{flow } R = Av = \frac{\pi 1.0 \text{ in.}^2}{4} \ \frac{1 \text{ ft}^2}{144 \text{ in.}^2} \ 31.9 \text{ ft/sec} = 0.174 \text{ ft}^3/\text{sec}$$

$$= 0.174 \text{ ft}^3 \ \frac{1 \text{ gal}}{0.1337 \text{ ft}^3} \ \frac{3600 \text{ sec}}{\text{hr}} = 4\overline{7}00 \text{ gal/hr}.$$

Fluid friction is measured in terms of the *coefficient of viscosity* η, which is defined as the ratio of the tangential force per unit area of surface, F/A, to the velocity gradient, v/s, between two planes of fluid in laminar flow:

$$\eta = \frac{Fs}{Av}. \tag{9-9}$$

Cohesion is the attraction between like molecules, while *adhesion* is the attraction between unlike molecules. At the surface of a liquid there is a *surface tension*. It is expressed as the force per unit length of the surface film:

$$T = \frac{F}{L}. \tag{9-10}$$

Surface tension is usually expressed in dynes per centimeter.

When a liquid is in contact with a solid, the liquid comes to the surface at a definite angle θ, called the *angle of contact*. Liquids that "wet" a surface have contact angles greater than $90°$.

Liquids rise or are depressed in fine (capillary) tubes. The height to which they rise is given by

$$h = \frac{2T \cos \theta}{r \rho g}. \qquad (9\text{-}11)$$

Example: A square 2.0 cm on a side, made of thin wire, is suspended from a balance in a horizontal position close to the surface of a liquid. It is dipped under the surface, then slowly raised. The liquid clings to the wire and forms a vertical double film just before it breaks. A 0.50-gm force is required to balance this film. What is the surface tension of the liquid?

The periphery of the wire square = 8.0 cm. Since there is a *double* film,

$$16T = (\tfrac{1}{2}) \ 980 \ \text{dynes},$$

$$T = 490 \ \text{dynes}/16 \ \text{cm} = 31 \ \text{dynes/cm}.$$

PROBLEMS

Buoyancy, Archimedes' principle

9-1. A stone weighs 0.54 newton in air and 0.34 newton when totally immersed in water. (a) What is its density? (b) What is the volume of the stone? (c) How much would the stone weigh when totally immersed in ethyl alcohol, whose density is 0.81 gm/cm^3? (*Ans:* 2.7 gm/cm^3; 200 cm^3; 378 gm)

9-2. A weighted glass bulb has a volume of 700.0 cm^3 at 20.0°C. It weighs 1.0100 gm when completely immersed in water at 20.0°C. The density of water at 20°C is 0.998229 gm/cm^3; and at 4°C it is 1.000,000 gm/cm^3. The coefficient of linear thermal expansion of the glass is 2.5×10^{-6} per °C. (a) What is the weight of water displaced by the bulb at 20°C when completely immersed? (b) What is the weight of the bulb in vacuum? (c) What is the volume of the bulb at 4°C? (d) What is the weight of the water displaced by the bulb at 4°C when completely immersed? (e) How much does the bulb weigh when completely immersed in water at 4°C?

9-3. The distance between the marks on the uniform stem of a hydrometer representing specific gravities of 0.90 and 1.10 respectively is 2.00 cm. (a) What length of stem represents the volume of that part of the hydrometer below the 1.10 mark? (b) How far above or below the 1.10 mark would the mark for a specific gravity of 1.20 be?

9-4. A 0.60-lb ball is inflated to a gauge pressure of 60 lb/in.^{2} for use in a water polo game. The internal volume of the ball is then 300 in.^{3} and the air is sealed in with a metal plunger 0.125 in. in diameter forced into the valve stem. (a) What force must be applied to hold the metal plunger in place? (b) What force must be exerted to submerge the ball in water (sp. gr. = 1.03)? Neglect the thickness of the rubber. (c) What volume would the air in the ball occupy if it were released to the atmosphere, if the ball is completely collapsed? (d) Would the ball weigh more when collapsed than when inflated? Why? (*Ans*: 7.5 lb; 10 lb; 1500 in.^{3})

9-5. What is the area of the smallest floating block of ice 4.0 in. thick that will just support a 160-lb man if the specific gravity of ice is 0.917 and the density of the water in which the ice is floating is 62.4 lb/ft^3?

9-6. A block of steel (sp. gr. = 7.8) of volume 10.0 cm^3 floats on the surface of mercury (sp. gr. = 13.6) contained in a vessel. What volume of platinum (sp. gr. = 21.4) suspended from the steel block will just submerge the block?

9-7. A 288-ton submarine lies just awash with its main diving tanks empty. If the motors are disabled, so that the submarine can submerge only vertically, what should be the capacity of the main diving tanks, if they can be filled instantly, for the sub to be able to sink 100 ft in 6.0 sec? Neglect friction of the water; take the density of sea water = 63 lb/ft^3. (*Ans*: 1.9×10^3 ft^3)

9-8. A layer of water is floating on top of mercury. A cylindrical block, axis vertical, of metal of density 7.30 gm/cm^3 and length 6.00 cm is floating so that its top projects 0.945 cm above the upper surface of the water. When oil to a depth of 1.00 cm is poured on top of the water, the top of the cylinder is level with the upper surface of the oil. Find (a) the density of the oil, (b) the thickness of the water layer. (*Ans*: 0.748 gm/cm^3, 1.98 cm)

9-9. A polar bear jumps on an iceberg and notices that his 400-lb weight is just sufficient to sink the iceberg. Water weighs 62.4 lb/ft^3 and ice has a density of 0.90 relative to water. What is the weight of the iceberg?

9-10. A 10-lb iron ball, specific gravity 7.8, is supported by a wire in fresh water. Determine the tension in the wire. (*Ans*: 8.7 lb)

9-11. An empty 5-gal gasoline can weighs 10 lb. While it is full of gasoline (sp. gr. = 0.75) it is accidentally dropped overboard into a fresh water lake. Will it sink or float? Why? (1 gal = 231 in.^{3})

9-12. A cubical block of wood 10.0 cm on a side floats at the interface between oil and water as indicated in Fig. 9-3 with its lower surface 2.0 cm below the interface. The density of oil is 0.60 gm/cm³. (a) What is the mass of the block? (b) What is the gauge pressure at the top of the block? (c) What is the gauge pressure at

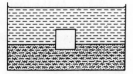

Fig. 9-3

the bottom of the block? (d) What is the force on one side of the block?

9-13. A balloon filled with hydrogen weighs 120 lb and contains 100 yd³ of gas. The air is at 0°C, 760 mm of mercury pressure, and density 2.2 lb/yd³. Under these conditions, what is the maximum load the balloon can lift? What will be the volume of the balloon if it rises to a height where the temperature is 0°C and the pressure is 3/5 of one atmosphere?

9-14. One arm of an open U-tube contains a column of mercury 5.0 cm high, the other a column of gasoline 92 cm high. Determine the specific gravity of the gasoline.

9-15. A rubber balloon filled with air is fixed to the bottom of a lake by a wire such that the balloon is 50 ft below the surface of the water (Fig. 9-4). The balloon has a weight of 0.10 lb and a volume of 1.20 ft³ (at the 50-ft depth). (a) What is the tension in the wire? (b) The unstretched length of the wire is 20 ft, its Young's modulus is 10⁶ lb/in.², its cross-sectional area is 0.001 in. How much is the wire stretched under this tension? (c) If the atmospheric pressure above the lake increases, in what way would the tension in the wire be affected? Explain clearly.

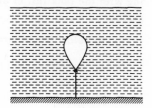

Fig. 9-4

Pressure, atmospheric

9-16. The three pieces of apparatus shown in Fig. 9-5 are all located in the same room. (a) What is the absolute pressure in flask A? (b) What is the absolute pressure in flask B? Explain how you obtain your answers.

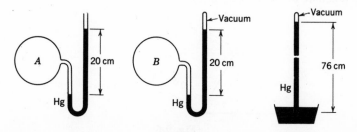

Fig.. 9-5

9-17. At the foot of a hill a barometer reads 29.0 in. and at the summit it reads 27.0 in. Assuming that the average density of the air between the two places is 0.080 lb/ft³, what is the height of the hill?

9-18. As a tornado passes by, the atmospheric pressure may very suddenly drop 0.4 in. of mercury. In a house whose doors, windows, and other openings are tightly shut, calculate the force this would cause on a window 2.5 ft square. What probably would happen to the window?

9-19. One end of a rubber tube is connected to the gas line of a laboratory and the other end is pushed under the surface of the water in a pail. When the open end of the tube is 8 in. below the surface of the water, the gas ceases to bubble from the end of the tube. Compute the gauge pressure of the gas in the mains in lb/in.². One cubic foot of water weighs 62.4 lb.

9-20. The water tank for a farm water system has a capacity of 30 gal. The water is forced into the tank and compresses the air in the top of the tank. The automatic switch shuts off the pump when the pressure builds up to 45 lb/in.² as read on the gauge connected to the tank. Starting with the tank full of air at atmospheric pressure (15 lb/in.²), how many gallons of water must be pumped into the tank before the switch trips off?

Pressure below liquid surface

9-21. A water-tight cubical box 2.0 m on a side has fitted to it a pipe of 1.0 cm² cross section extending upward for 12 m above the top of the box. This system is completely filled with water. Find the pressure on the bottom of the box.

9-22. The Kelvin depth gauge consists of a tube 2 ft in length and of uniform bore, sealed at the top and coated on the inside with a soluble substance to indicate the height to which water has entered. It was found upon raising the tube after a sounding in the ocean that the water had risen to a point 3.0 in. from the closed top. To what depth had the gauge been immersed? (The barometer read 30 in. at the time; the specific gravity of sea water is 1.03.) (*Ans:* $\overline{2}30$ ft)

9-23. In a certain home the faucet in the kitchen sink is 110 ft below the level of the water in the tower supplying the pressure. How much is the pressure at the faucet, in lb/in.²?

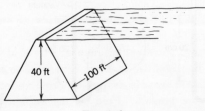

Fig. 9-6

Dam

9-24. A dam 100 ft long is 40 ft high and has a symmetrical cross section 5.0 ft thick at the top and 65 ft thick at the base (Fig. 9-6). The water extends to the top of the dam. Find (a) the pressure at the bottom of the dam, (b) the total hydrostatic force on the dam, (c) the torque tending to overturn the dam.

9-25. Find the force acting on a triangular-shaped dam filled with water to its top. The dam has the dimensions shown in Fig. 9-7.

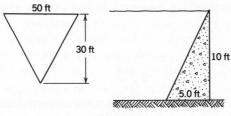

Fig. 9-7

9-26. A dam is 30 ft in length and has a vertical height of 10 ft. Its cross section is a right triangle of 5.0-ft base. If the water extends to the top of the dam, in contact with the sloping side, what is the force tending to slide the dam off its foundation? What is the torque tending to overturn the dam?

Pascal's law

9-27. A 200-lb man sits on a barber chair which, together with its 10-in. diameter hydraulic plunger, weighs 200 lb. The barber wishes to raise the chair a distance of 3.0 in., using a class one lever with an IMA of 0.50, connected to a pump with a bore of 1.0 in. and a stroke of 4.0 in. Assuming no losses, how much work must be done? (*Ans*: $\overline{10}0$ ft-lb)

9-28. A hydraulic press has two cylinders with diameters of 4.0 cm and 20.0 cm, respectively. What is (a) the theoretical mechanical advantage, and (b) the force required on the smaller piston to raise a car having a mass of 2000 kg?

Fluid flow, Bernoulli's equation

9-29. What are the defining characteristics of streamline or steady flow of a fluid?

9-30. It is desired to refuel a plane at a rate of 50 gal/min (1 ft³ = 7.5 gal). The fuel line is a 3.0-in. hose connected to a pump 3.0 ft above the ground, and a 2.0-in. nozzle delivering gasoline (sp. gr. = 0.72) to the plane 15 ft above the ground. Find (a) the velocity of the fuel at the nozzle, (b) the velocity of the fuel in the line near the pump, (c) the pressure in the line near the pump.

9-31. Compute the friction head between a reservoir and a hydrant 150 ft below. The pressure at the hydrant is 50 lb/in.²

9-32. During construction of a building, mortar (in a fluid state) was pumped into a flexible hose 5.0 in. in diameter and discharged from a nozzle 3.0 in. in diameter on the second floor, 21 ft above the pump. The mortar weighed 150 lb/ft³ and was discharged at the rate of 45 ft³/min. As an approximation, assume no frictional losses and find (a) the velocity of the mortar at the nozzle, (b) the velocity of the mortar entering the hose, and (c) the pressure in the hose at the pump.

9-33. If a gauge which measures hydrostatic pressure is placed on the sea bottom in shallow water there is an increase in pressure when a ship passes directly over it. (a) Use Bernoulli's principle to explain why this happens. (You may consider the ship fixed and the water flowing past.) (b) Explain qualitatively how you would expect this pressure increase to vary with the depth of the water and the ship's speed and size.

9-34. A water main 8.0-in. in diameter has a constriction 6.0 in. in diameter. (a) When the pressure in the main is 80 lb/in.² and the pressure in the constriction is 60 lb/in.², how many cubic feet per minute are flowing in the water line? (b) What is the velocity of the water in the constriction?

9-35. Water is flowing downward through an insulated vertical pipe which at one point narrows to 1/3 of the cross-sectional area at the top of the pipe. If the pressure of the water at the constriction is 1.0 atm and the temperature is 20.0°C, and at a point 10 m above the constriction the pressure is 4.5 atm and the temperature is 19.9°C, what is the speed of the water in the constriction? (*Ans*: 8$\overline{4}$0 cm/sec)

9-36. Water is flowing in a pipe of radius of 4.0 in. at a pressure of 1000 lb/ft² and with a velocity of 20.0 ft/sec. What will be the pressure if the pipe increases to a radius of 6.0 in. and drops 50.0 ft in elevation?

9-37. A horizontal line of cross sectional area 10.0 in.² has a constriction of cross section 5.0 in.². If the flow of water in the pipe is streamline, and its speed in the constriction is 10 ft/sec, what will be the speed of the water in the portion of larger cross section?

9-38. A pitot tube (used to measure speed relative to a fluid) consists of two tubes connected to a pressure gauge, as shown in Fig. 9-8. The fluid in the inner tube A is at rest. If mercury is used in the U-tube

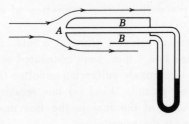

Fig. 9-8

pressure gauge, what speed (in mi/hr) of air past tube B will produce a difference of 1.0 in. in the mercury columns? Assume that density of air is 0.080 lb/ft³ and that the sp. gr. of mercury $= 13.6$.

9-39. Assume that air flows past the wing of an airplane with streamline flow. (a) If the velocity of flow over the lower surface of the wings of a plane is 300 ft/sec, what is the required speed over the upper surface to support a plane weighing 2000 lb having a wing area of 200 ft²? The density of air may be assumed constant and equal to 2.4×10^{-3} slug/ft³. (b) What is the pressure difference between the top and the bottom of a wing, expressed as a fraction of normal atmospheric pressure of 15 lb/in.²?

Velocity of efflux, Torricelli's equation

9-40. You and Lana Turner are shipwrecked on a South Sea Island. By chance, she finds a tin can of square cross-sectional area 40×40 cm and of height 70 cm lying on the beach. You decide to make a shower out of it by punching 20 holes, each of 0.10 cm² area, into the bottom of the can. If she likes to stay in the shower for 5 min, does the can have sufficient capacity? (*Ans:* Yes, if filled to a height of 69 cm)

9-41. A pump at the base of a full tank of water 10 ft square and 20 ft high is to deliver water 90 ft above the pump with an exit velocity of 16 ft/sec. The pump and motor combination is 50% efficient. When the pump is started, the reading of the meter in the electric service line to the motor is 37,735.4 kwh. What is the meter reading when the tank is empty? (*Ans:* 37,743.3 kwh)

9-42. The level of water in a storage tank is 40 ft above the opening of a faucet. If air pressure of 60 lb/in.² is maintained above the water in the tank, and assuming no frictional losses, with what speed will the water flow from the cpen faucet? (*Ans:* 106.8 ft/sec)

9-43. A tank is filled to a depth of 10 ft with salt water having a sp. gr. of 1.10. With what speed will the water flow from a small hole in the side of the tank 2.0 ft from its bottom?

9-44. How long does it take to empty a water tank of cross-sectional area 10,000 cm² and height 1860 cm through a hole in the bottom of effective area 100 cm²?

Siphon

9-45. How far below the level of the water in the upper cistern must the lower opening of a siphon be for the water to flow out through a tube of cross section 0.50 cm² with a speed of 330 cm/sec? (b) What is the rate of flow in liters/min? (c) What would be the effect on the answers to (a) and (b) if the water were replaced by kerosene, which has sp. gr. of 0.90?

Turbine

9-46. Water falls from a height of 60.0 ft and drives a water turbine. If the flow rate is 480 ft/min, determine the maximum horsepower that can be produced. (*Ans:* 54.4 hp)

9-47. Water having a total head of 80.0 ft is delivered to a turbine at the rate of 55.1 ft^3/sec. The turbine delivers a torque of 1750.0 lb-ft at 1200 rev/min. (a) What is the horsepower output of the turbine? (b) What is its efficiency?

Pressure, bulk modulus

9-48. A volume of 2000 cm^3 of water is reduced to 1980 cm^3 by an increase in pressure of 3400 lb/in.^{2}. What are (a) the stress, (b) the strain, (c) the bulk modulus of the water, and (d) the compressibility of the water?

9-49. The bulk modulus of water is 3.1×10^5 lb/in.^{2}. Compute the pressure change necessary to produce a change of 0.10% in a given volume of water.

Viscosity

9-50. How does viscosity vary with the temperature for (a) liquids, (b) gases?

Surface tension; capillarity

9-51. Why is it that there is a capillary rise in a tube dipping into water, and a capillary depression in a tube dipping into mercury?

9-52. Figure 9-9 is an enlarged view of a capillary tube. Points a and c are just outside the liquid surface, and points b and d are just inside. Answer the following questions concerning the pressure at each of the points given. Which is greater, or are they equal: (a) p_a or p_b? (b) p_b or p_d? (c) p_d or p_e? (d) p_b or p_e? Explain.

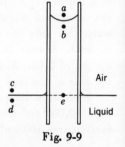
Fig. 9-9

9-53. A liquid with a sp. gr. of 0.80 rises to a height of 10 cm in a capillary tube of radius 0.050 mm. If the angle of contact is 60°, find the surface tension of the liquid.

9-54. A small cube of side a floats in a liquid of density ρ and surface tension T. The angle of contact between the liquid and the cube is θ. If the bottom of the cube is a distance h below the surface level of the water, what is the density of the cube?

9-55. Two clean glass plates are separated by a very small angle ϕ and are placed vertically in a tank of water (Fig. 9-10). Assuming that

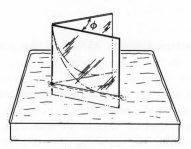

Fig. 9-10

θ, the angle of contact between water and plate, is constant, find the height of the capillary rise as a function of the distance from the junction.

9-56. To what height will a liquid of sp. gr. 0.80 and surface tension 49 dynes/cm rise between two vertical parallel glass plates 0.50 mm apart, due to capillary action? (The angle of contact is zero degrees.)

9-57. A smooth spherical ball of density 0.46 gm/cm³ is wet by water, and is observed to float on a water surface exactly half submerged. If, for the water, $T = 70$ erg/cm², what is the radius of the ball? (Ans: 1.6 cm)

9-58. Carbon tetrachloride flows steadily through a horizontal cylindrical tube of diameter 1.0 cm. The pressure difference between two points in the tube as measured by the manometer shown in Fig. 9-11 is

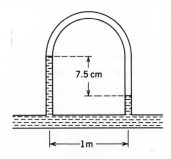

7.5 cm

1 m

Fig. 9-11

7.5 cm of CCl₄. If the density of the CCl₄ is 1.6 gm/cm³ and the rate of flow in the tube is 250 cm³/sec, what is the coefficient of viscosity of the CCl₄? (This is a standard method of measuring viscosity, developed by Poiseuille.) (Ans: 1.1 × 10⁻² poise)

9-59. By means of two parallel coaxial wire loops, each 2.0 cm in diameter, a soap bubble with cylindrical sides and spherical ends is formed. What is the radius of curvature of the spherical ends? (Ans: 2.0 cm)

9-60. Calculate the excess pressure inside a raindrop 4.0 mm in diameter. (*Ans:* 730 dynes/cm²)

9-61. When the temperature is 27°C and the pressure inside a partially evacuated bell jar is 76 mm of mercury, a soap bubble inside the jar is observed to have a radius of 1.0 mm. If the temperature inside the jar rises to 77°C, what must the pressure inside the bell jar be adjusted to so that the bubble stays the same size? For soap solution, take T at 27°C to be 70 dynes/cm, at 77°C to be 40 dynes/cm. (*Ans:* 90 mm of Hg)

9-62. A bubble of glycerin has a diameter of 0.50 cm. If the pressure inside the bubble is greater than the outside pressure by 1.0 mm, find the surface tension of glycerin. Density of mercury is 13.6 gm/cm³.

9-63. An inverted U-shaped wire having a length of 8.0 cm is lowered into a liquid at 20°C. What is the surface tension of the liquid if, as the wire is removed, it takes a force of 380 dynes to break the film formed in the loop?

9-64. A circular iron wire loop 5.0 cm in diameter and weighing 2.0 gm is to be pressed down into the surface of a dish of mercury. If the specific gravity of iron is 7.8 and the plane of the loop is parallel to the surface of the mercury, find (a) the value of the buoyant force when the wire is submerged, and (b) the force due to surface tension just before the loop submerges. (The surface tension of mercury is 530 dynes/cm.)

Mechanics

PART A

In the following 16 items, put the *letter* corresponding to the best completion in the blank at the right of the item number. Work need not be shown. Each item counts 2 points.

1. .... The term which is most nearly identical with mass is (A) force, (B) inertia, (C) weight, (D) volume.

2. .... The height of a medium-sized man might be (A) 170 cm, (B) 225 cm, (C) 100 cm, (D) 71 cm.

3. .... A man who can lift a maximum of 150 lb could lift a maximum of (A) 15 kg, (B) 46 kg, (C) 68 kg, (D) 240 kg.

4. .... Two vector quantities, whose directions may be altered at will, may have a resultant of any magnitude between the limits 0 and 100. The magnitude of each vector quantity *must* therefore be (A) between 0 and 40, (B) 50, (C) between 60 and 100, (D) less than 50.

5. .... A bird lights on a stretched telegraph wire. The additional tension produced in the wire is (A) zero, (B) less than the weight of the bird, (C) equal to the weight of the bird, (D) greater than the weight of the bird.

6. .... The acceleration of a falling body is 32 ft/sec². This means that (A) it will fall 32 ft during each second, (B) it will fall 32 ft during the first second, from rest, (C) it will increase its velocity by 32 ft/sec during each second, (D) its acceleration increases 32 ft/sec² during each second.

7. .... Two bodies, *A* and *B*, are falling, with negligible air resistance, side by side above a horizontal plane. If body *A* is given a horizontal acceleration, (A) it will fall more slowly, (B) both bodies will strike the plane at the same time, (C) the vertical motion of body *A* will be altered, (D) the vertical components of motion will be unequal.

8. .... The force of gravity on a body is (A) independent of the mass of the body, (B) equal to 980 dynes (C) proportional to the mass of the body, (D) equal to 980 cm/sec².

9. .... According to one of Newton's Laws of Motion, a body upon which no external force acts must (A) remain at rest or move with a con-

stant speed in a straight line, (B) fall toward the earth, (C) gradually
come to rest, (D) have an equal and opposite reaction.

10. .... A force gives a certain mass an acceleration a. The force is
tripled and the mass is reduced to 1/3 its former value. The acceleration will now be (A) $3a$, (B) $6a$, (C) $9a$, (D) $27a$.

11. .... If a raindrop with a mass of 0.05 gm falls with constant
speed, the retarding force of atmospheric friction is (A) 49 dynes, (B) 480
dynes, (C) 980 dynes, (D) 0.05 dyne.

12. .... The net force acting upon a particle of mass 10-gm traveling
with a constant velocity of 5 cm/sec is (A) 50 dynes, (B) 10 dynes,
(C) zero, (D) 50 gm-cm/sec.

13. .... At a point where the acceleration due to gravity is 981
cm/sec^2, the earth will pull on a mass of 100 gm with a force of (A) 100
dynes, (B) 981 dynes, (C) 100/32 dynes, (D) 98,100 dynes.

14. .... If 50 dynes of force are exerted on a free mass of 100 gm for
4 sec the total change in velocity is (A) 4 cm/sec, (B) 2 cm/sec,
(C) 2/980 cm/sec, (D) 4/980 cm/sec.

15. .... If a man of mass m is carried by an elevator with upward acceleration a the magnitude of the force which he exerts on the floor is
(A) mg, (B) $m(g + a)$, (C) $m(g - a)$, (D) mga.

16. .... If the earth's mass and radius were each doubled, the weight
of a 100-lb boy would then become (A) 200 lb, (B) 400 lb, (C) 50 lb,
(D) 100 lb.

PART B

Put the solutions of the following questions in your "blue-book."
The work must be shown. Start each question on a new page. State
units in all cases.

1. (a) Using a freehand sketch, show clearly how to find the resultant
R of the three forces shown in Fig. 1 by the *vector polygon method*.

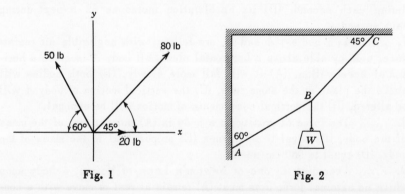

Fig. 1   Fig. 2

(b) Calculate R_x and R_y, the x- and y-components of the resultant of these three forces, by the analytical component method.

2. Three ropes are knotted at B and tied as in Fig. 2 to the wall and ceiling of a room. The tension in AB is 540 lb. Find the weight of W.

3. The 4000-gm mass in Fig. 3 is drawn up the inclined plane with an acceleration of 245 cm/sec² by the string which is attached to m_2. (a) Find the tension in the string. (b) Find the mass m_2.

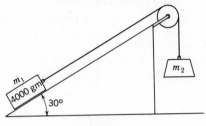

Fig. 3

4. A body is projected with a speed of 100 ft/sec at an angle θ above the horizontal (sin $\theta = 0.6$, cos $\theta = 0.8$). For a time 3 sec later, find (a) the horizontal and vertical components of its velocity, (b) the horizontal and vertical distances from the starting point.

5. Starting with the definitions of acceleration and average velocity, show that a body with constant acceleration experiences a displacement s given by:

$$s = v_1 t + \tfrac{1}{2} at^2.$$

Mechanics

Sample Final Examination (2 hr)

This Examination has two parts: A and B. If an answer has units, you must include the units. Factors of π may be left in the answer, e.g., 17π. In Part A, each answer counts 4 points.

PART A

1. A mass m is acted upon by a force F while moving through a horizontal displacement s. Its gravitational potential energy is thereby changed by an amount (A) zero, (B) Fs, (C) mgs, (D) $\frac{1}{2}mv^2$, (E) ms.

2. A load hanging from a steel wire causes the wire to stretch a certain amount. The same load, hanging from a steel wire of twice the length but the same diameter, will cause the wire to stretch (A) 1/4 as much, (B) 1/2 as much, (C) the same amount, (D) twice as much, (E) four times as much.

3. A cylindrical disk has a moment of inertia $(1/2)\ mR^2$ and a constant angular velocity ω. Its rotational kinetic energy is (a) $\frac{1}{2}mR^2\omega^2$, (b) $\frac{1}{4}mR^2\omega^2$, (c) $\frac{1}{2}mR^2\omega$, (d) $\frac{1}{4}mR^2\omega$, (e) $\frac{1}{2}m\omega^2$.

4. A sphere of mass m and moment of inertia I is initially at rest at the top of an inclined plane, of height h. (a) What is its potential energy at the top of the incline? (b) What is its potential energy at the instant it reaches the bottom? (c) At the instant the sphere reaches the bottom, is its *translational* kinetic energy less than, equal to, or greater than its initial potential energy?

5. A particle of mass 3 gm is moving with a constant speed of 4 cm/sec around the circumference of a circle of radius 8 cm. Calculate the magnitude of (a) the kinetic energy of the particle, (b) the moment of inertia of the particle with respect to an axis through the center of the circle, (c) the acceleration of the particle, (d) the force required, if any, to keep the particle moving around the circle, (e) the angular velocity of the particle with respect to the center of the circle.

PART B

1. A 5.0-gm particle, possessing a kinetic energy of 1000 ergs, collides with a 15.0-gm particle which is initially at rest. If the collision is completely inelastic, that is, the particles stick together after the collision, then calculate: (a) the velocities of the particles after the collision, (b) the kinetic energy lost as a consequence of the collision.

2. A uniform ladder, 40 ft long and weighing 60 lb, rests on the ground without slipping and leans against a smooth vertical wall. The angle between the ladder and wall is $30°$. A 200-lb man is standing on the ladder at a point 8.0 ft from the top of the ladder. (a) Find the vertical component V of the force exerted by the ground on the ladder, (b) Find the force F exerted by the wall on the ladder, (c) Find the horizontal component H of the force exerted by the ground on the ladder.

3. (a) Define simple harmonic motion. (b) A gust of wind bends a tree so that the tree top is displaced a distance of 5 ft from its normal position. Thereupon, the tree sways back and forth, essentially in a straight line, taking 4 sec for one complete oscillation. Assume that the motion of the tree is simple harmonic. (1) At what point will the tree top be moving fastest? (2) Find the maximum speed of the tree top. (3) At what point will the acceleration of the tree be a maximum? (4) Find the maximum acceleration of the tree top.

4. A cylinder 16 cm in diameter is mounted, with its axis horizontal, on bearings having negligible friction. It is free to rotate about its axis. A string is wrapped around the cylinder; when a body of mass m is hung on the string, the angular acceleration produced is 12.0 rad/sec^2 and the tension in the string is 150,000 dynes. (a) Calculate the moment of inertia of the cylinder. (b) Calculate the magnitude of the mass m hanging from the string.

Mechanics

Sample Final Examination (2 hr)

Answer any eight questions:

1. In Fig. 1, neglect the weight of the boom and find (a) the tension in the guy wire, and (b) the resultant force exerted by the mast, at A, on the boom.

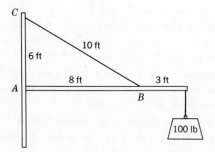

Fig. 1

2. Concrete (sp. gr. = 3.5) is pumped through a pipe to a point 50 ft above the pump. The outlet end of the pipe has a diameter of 8.0 in. and the diameter at the pump is 6.0 in. Concrete is to be delivered at the rate of 28 ft³/min. Neglect frictional losses and find (a) the horsepower output of the pump, (b) the speed of the concrete at the outlet, (c) the pressure at the pump.

3. A simple pendulum, consisting of a bob of mass 120-gm suspended by a 60-cm length of light string, is oscillating with an amplitude of 15°. Find (a) the maximum potential energy of the bob, (b) the maximum speed of the bob, (c) the tension in the string at the instant it makes an angle of 10° with the vertical, (d) the speed of the bob at that instant, and (e) the period of oscillation of the pendulum.

4. A solid steel sphere, 3.0 ft³ in volume, is suspended by means of a $\frac{1}{2}$-in. steel cable at a depth of 2500 ft in sea water (sp. gr. = 1.03). For steel, $\alpha = 11 \times 10^{-6}/°C$, sp. gr. = 7.8, $Y = 30 \times 10^6$ lb/in.², $B = 18 \times 10^6$ lb/in.². Find (a) the tension in the cable, (b) the elongation of the cable, (c) the change in temperature that would produce the same elongation,

(d) the pressure on the sphere, (e) the change in volume of the sphere due to the pressure.

5. In Fig. 2, a 2000-gm solid sphere of 15 cm radius is located on a 25° incline at a point 51 cm above the floor. Assume that the sphere rolls but that frictional losses are negligible. For a sphere, $I = \frac{2}{5}mR^2$. Find (a) the torque acting on the sphere, (b) its angular acceleration, (c) its linear speed when it reaches the floor.

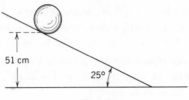

51 cm

25°

Fig. 2

6. A 25-gm lead bullet at 20°C strikes a fixed target. For lead, melting point = 261°F, heat of fusion = 5.4 cal/gm, specific heat = 0.032. (a) Find the heat required to melt the bullet. (b) If 80% of the heat generated upon impact goes into the bullet, what must be its initial velocity for the bullet to melt upon striking the target?

7. A block weighing 4.0 lb is whirled in a vertical circle whose center is 10 ft above the ground. The string by means of which the block is being whirled is 3.0 ft long. The string breaks when the block has acquired a speed of 30 ft/sec. Find (a) the tensile strength of the string, (b) the distance x, indicated in Fig. 3, to the point where the block hits the ground, and (c) the resultant velocity of the block when it hits the ground.

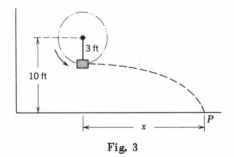

3 ft

10 ft

x P

Fig. 3

(d) Assume that upon hitting the ground, the block immediately loses its vertical component of motion but that the horizontal component is unchanged by the impact. Find the distance the block will slide along the ground from point P if $\mu = 0.38$, between the block and the ground.

8. Data from rocket flights indicate that at an altitude of 120 km above the earth the atmospheric pressure is 0.30×10^{-4} mm of mercury

and the temperature is 300 °K. These flights also seem to indicate no appreciable change in the composition of the atmosphere. At standard conditions air has a density of 1.293 gm/liter. Find (a) the density of air at 120 km, (b) the rms speed of an "air molecule" at 120 km, (c) the kinetic energy of a nitrogen molecule at such a speed (the molecular weight M_2 is 28.0).

9. (a) For a gas undergoing an adiabatic compression, show that the bulk modulus, $B = \gamma p$. (b) Assuming that the velocity of a compressional wave in a gas is given by $v = \sqrt{B/d}$, show that $v = \sqrt{\gamma R T}$.

10. (a) Prove that the motion described by the equation $x = r \sin \omega t$ is simple harmonic. (b) Derive the formula for the period of vibration of such motion. (c) Prove that a simple pendulum approximates SHM.

11. (a) Prove that for any rigid body $I = \Sigma \, mr^2$. (b) Why must the body be rigid for the formula to apply?

12. Define (a) an adiabatic process, (b) torque, (c) moment of inertia, (d) work, (e) British thermal unit, (f) efficiency, (g) actual mechanical advantage, (h) impulse, (i) simple harmonic motion, (j) pressure (average).

Part II

WAVE MOTION; SOUND

CHAPTER 1

Wave Motion

Wave motion is the propagation of a temporary change in the shape or condition of a medium through the medium, with the transmission of energy outward from the source.

The deformation may be a single pulse or it may be a succession of periodic disturbances, called a *wave train*.

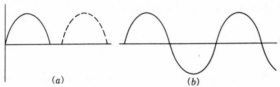

Fig. 1-1. (a) Wave pulse; (b) wave train.

In *transverse* waves, the particles of the medium vibrate in paths perpendicular to the direction in which the wave moves. In *longitudinal* waves the paths in which the particles vibrate are parallel to the direction of the wave. In a *torsional* wave a twist is propagated through the medium.

The *speed* of a wave, or its velocity of propagation, is the distance the wave form moves per unit time. The speed depends upon the kind of wave and the properties of the medium. For a transverse wave in a string

$$v = \sqrt{\frac{F}{m/l}}. \tag{1-1}$$

For a compressional wave in a solid

$$v = \sqrt{\frac{Y}{\rho}}. \tag{1-2}$$

For a compressional wave in a fluid

$$v = \sqrt{\frac{B}{\rho}}. \tag{1-3}$$

Example: A cord 75 cm long has a mass of 0.252 gm. It is stretched by a load of 2.0 kg. What is the speed of a transverse wave in this cord?

$$v = \sqrt{\frac{F}{m/l}}, \quad \frac{m}{l} = \frac{0.252 \text{ gm}}{80 \text{ cm}} = 0.0034 \text{ gm/cm},$$

$$F = mg = 2000 \text{ gm} \times 980 \text{ cm/sec}^2,$$

$$v = \sqrt{\frac{1.96 \times 10^6 \text{ gm-cm}}{\sec^2 0.0034 \text{ gm/cm}}} = 2\overline{4}0 \text{ m/sec}.$$

Example: Find the speed of a compressional wave in a steel rail whose density is 490 lb/ft^3 and whose Young's modulus is 29×10^6 lb/in.^{2}.

$$v = \sqrt{\frac{Y}{\rho}} = \sqrt{\frac{29 \times 10^6 \times 144 \text{ lb/ft}^2 \,(32 \text{ ft/sec}^2)}{490 \text{ lb/ft}^3}} = 1\overline{6},500 \text{ ft/sec}.$$

The transverse *displacement* y of a particle in a sinusoidal wave at time t and at distance x from the origin is

$$y = y_0 \sin \frac{2\pi}{\lambda} (x - vt), \tag{1-4}$$

Frequency f is the number of waves per second which pass a point.
Period T is the time required for one wave to pass the point in question.

$$f = \frac{1}{T}. \tag{1-5}$$

Wavelength λ is the distance between two adjacent particles in the same phase.

Speed v, frequency f, and wavelength λ, are related by the expression

$$v = f\lambda.$$

Two particles are in the same *phase* if they have the same displacement from the equilibrium position and are moving in the same direction.
Amplitude is the maximum displacement of a particle in a wave motion.

For a sound wave in a gas, the compressions are adiabatic, and this leads to a dependence of speed on temperature:

$$v = \sqrt{\frac{p_0 \gamma}{\rho_0}} = \sqrt{\gamma RT}, \tag{1-6}$$

where p_0 is the absolute equilibrium pressure (lb/ft^2, newtons/m^2, ...).

Example: Compute the speed of sound waves in air at 20°C. The average molecular weight of air is 29, $\gamma = 1.40$, and $R = 8.3 \times 10^7$ ergs/mole °K.

$$v = \left[\frac{1.40 \times 10^7 \text{ ergs} \times 293\,^\circ\text{K}}{\text{mole } ^\circ\text{K } (29 \text{ gm/mole})} \right]^{1/2} = 3\overline{4}0 \text{ m/sec} = 1\overline{1}20 \text{ ft/sec.}$$

This result is in good agreement with the measured speed of sound at this temperature.

In acoustical engineering one is more often concerned with the pressure variations in a sound wave than with the actual displacements of the air particles (Eq. 1-4). The two are related by:

$$p = -\left[\frac{2\pi \rho_0 v^2 y}{\lambda} \right] \cos \frac{2\pi}{\lambda} (x - vt) = -P \cos \frac{2\pi}{\lambda} (x - vt). \qquad (1\text{-}7)$$

Here p represents the gauge pressure. The term in brackets is the maximum gauge pressure or the *pressure amplitude P*. The sound wave may be considered either as a displacement wave or as a pressure wave. If the former is written as a sine function, the latter will be a cosine function, and vice versa. The displacement wave is 90° out of phase with the pressure wave. Where the displacement is a maximum, the excess pressure is zero.

Example: Measurements of sound waves show that the maximum pressure variation, P, in the faintest 1000-cycle sound which can be heard is only 0.0002 dyne/cm². Find the corresponding displacement amplitude of the air particles.

From Eq. (1-7),

$$y_0 = \frac{P}{2\pi \rho_0 v^2},$$

$$\lambda = \frac{v}{f} = \frac{3\overline{4}0 \text{ m/sec}}{1000 \text{ vib/sec}} = 34 \text{ cm,}$$

$$y_0 = \frac{34 \text{ cm} \times (2 \times 10^{-4} \text{ dyne/cm}^2)}{2\pi\,(0.00122 \text{ gm/cm}^3)\,(3.43 \times 10^4 \text{ cm/sec})^2}$$

$$= 10^{-9} \text{ cm (approx.).}$$

PROBLEMS

1-1. List and discuss all the factors which determine the fundamental frequency of the transverse vibration of a stretched string.

1-2. A wire 3.0 ft long has a tension of 20 lb and a mass of 0.0040 lb/ft. (a) What is the velocity of a transverse wave on this wire? (b) What is the frequency of the third harmonic?

1-3. A traveling transverse wave on a string is represented by the equation

$$y = 3.0 \sin 30(t - 0.010\, x),$$

where t is in seconds and x is in centimeters. Calculate (a) the frequency, (b) the wavelength, and (c) the period. (d) What is the velocity of propagation of the wave? (e) What is the maximum transverse velocity of a particle of the string?

1-4. For a string of linear density ρ (gm/cm) and tension F (dynes), derive the equation

$$\frac{d^2 y}{dx} = \frac{\rho}{T(d^2 y/dt)}.$$

Indicate what assumptions and approximations are necessary.

1-5. A wave represented by the equation

$$y = a \sin \frac{2\pi}{\lambda}(x - vt)$$

is sent down a string stretched at tension T. The far end of the string is held fixed. What is the maximum transverse force on the end support? Assume T constant.

1-6. Standing waves are produced in a horizontally stretched rope, one end of which is fastened to the wall and the other to an eccentric on the shaft of a motor. If data were taken on corresponding values of the tension F in the rope and the angular speed ω of the motor, for a fixed distance d between nodes, what would be the nature of the graph obtained by plotting the data rectangularly? Sketch the graph and write the equation of the graph, in terms of the symbols given. Let m_1 be the mass per unit length of the rope.

1-7. The equation of a traveling wave in a particular string is $y_0 = 5.0 \sin 2\pi(t/0.080 - x/100)$, where x is measured in centimeters and t in seconds. (a) Find the velocity of propagation of the wave. (b) What is the velocity of a particle at $x = 0$ when 24 sec have passed since it was first displaced from rest?

1-8. Given a wave on an infinitely long vibrating string described by $y = y_0 \cos 2\pi/\lambda (x - vt)$. If the mass per unit length is m_1, find the total energy per unit length due to vibration of the string in terms of the amplitude, frequency, and m_1. Use the same approximations made in deriving the equation of motion of the string.

1-9. (a) Write the equation of a transverse wave which is moving in the positive x-direction if the velocity of the wave is 3000 cm/sec, the frequency is 100 cycles/sec, and the maximum amplitude is 0.10 cm. (b) If this wave is a transverse wave on a wire, what is the maximum velocity of a particle on the wire?

1-10. The equation of a transverse wave is $y = 2.0 \sin (60t - 0.20x)$, where x and y are in feet and t is in seconds. (a) What is the velocity of the wave? (b) What is the amplitude of the wave at the point $x = 55$ ft when $t = 0.20$ sec?

1-11. A particle is moving in simple harmonic motion. The amplitude is 0.10 cm and the frequency is 1000 cycles/sec. (a) Write an equation which gives the displacement at all times. (b) If the displacement is zero at time $t = 0$, at what time is the displacement 0.050 cm? (c) At what time is the acceleration numerically equal to the velocity?

1-12. A cord is stretched horizontally along the positive x-axis, with its end at the origin. The particle of cord at $x = 0$ is subjected simultaneously to two simple harmonic motions, both of which take place along the y-axis. The frequency of each motion is 8.0 vibrations/sec. One motion has an amplitude of 5.0 cm and the other an amplitude of 12 cm. The motion of 5-cm amplitude leads that of 12-cm amplitude by 90°. The velocity of a transverse wave in the cord is 75 cm/sec. (a) Describe as completely as you can the motion of the particle at $x = 0$. What is its maximum displacement? (b) What is the wavelength of the transverse wave in the cord? (c) At a particular instant, the particle at $x = 50$ cm has its maximum (positive) displacement. What is the least time interval before the particle at $x = 150$ cm has the same displacement? (d) At a particular instant, what is the phase difference between the particles mentioned in part (c)?

1-13. A cord is stretched along the positive x-axis with its end at the origin. This end of the cord is forced to vibrate transversely, such that its y- and z-coordinates are given by $y = 4.0 \sin (6\pi t + \pi)$ and $z = 10 \sin 3\pi t$, where y and z are in centimeters, and t in seconds. The velocity of a transverse wave in the cord is 60 cm/sec. (a) Using a geometric construction, find the particle path of motion of the particle at $x = 12$ cm. (b) Find the displacement of the particle at $x = 15$ cm at $t = 9.0$ sec. (c) Compute the first positive value of t for which the displacement of the particle at $x = 15$ cm is zero.

CHAPTER 2

Vibration of Strings and Air Columns

When two or more waves travel through the same medium they *interfere;* the motion of any given particle in the medium is a combination of the motions involved in each of the waves. The *principle of superposition,* applied to a string or an air column, expresses the fact that the actual displacement of any particle is the algebraic sum of the displacement of the individual waves.

Standing waves may result when two waves of the same frequency and amplitude travel in opposite directions through a medium. Certain points, known as the *nodes,* remain always at rest. Midway between the nodes, at the *loops* or *antinodes,* the vibrations are a maximum. The distance between successive nodes (or antinodes) is a half wavelength.

The analytical expression for a sinusoidal standing wave in a string can be derived by adding to the equation for the wave incident at one end of the string, the equation for the wave reflected at the other end (principle of superposition):

$$y = y_1 + y_2 = y_0 \left[\cos \frac{2\pi}{\lambda} (x - vt) - \cos \frac{2\pi}{\lambda} (x + vt) \right], \qquad (2\text{-}1)$$

which simplifies, by trigonometric relations, to

$$y = 2 y_0 \ \sin \frac{2\pi x}{\lambda} \sin 2\pi ft. \qquad (2\text{-}2)$$

For a string fixed at both ends, the ends must be nodes. Since the nodes are one-half wavelength apart, the length of the string may be $\lambda/2$, $2\lambda/2$, $3\lambda/2$, ..., or any integral number of half wavelengths. For a particular string of length L, standing waves may be set up by vibrations which give rise to waves of wavelengths $2L/1$, $2L/2$, $2L/3$ ... From the relation $f = v/\lambda$, the possible frequencies are $v/2L$, $2v/2L$, $3v/2L$, ... The lowest frequency, $v/2L$, is called the *fundamental* frequency, f_0, and the others are the *overtones:* $2f_0$, $3f_0$, ...

From $f_0 = v/2L$ and Eq. (1-1), it follows that the fundamental frequency of a vibrating string is

$$f_0 = \frac{1}{2L} \sqrt{\frac{F}{m/L}}. \tag{2-3}$$

A *harmonic* series refers to overtones whose frequencies are integral multiples of the fundamental. The frequency $2f_0$ is called the *first overtone* or the *second harmonic;* $3f_0$ is the *second overtone* or the *third harmonic,* and so on.

In strings or open-tube air columns, all harmonics are possible. In closed tubes, only the odd harmonics can occur.

When two sources of slightly different frequency are sounded simultaneously, the resultant amplitude fluctuates. These fluctuations are called *beats.* The number of beats per second equals the difference of the frequencies, $f_1 - f_2$.

PROBLEMS

Sound waves in a gas

2-1. How would an atmosphere of hydrogen affect the pitch of an organ pipe? Of a tuning fork?

2-2. When room temperature is $18\,^{\circ}$C, an organ and a piano are tuned to the same pitch so that they can be used in a duet. After the temperature rises to $26\,^{\circ}$C, will they sound all right if played together? Discuss as completely as possible, using equations.

2-3. We may think of the propagation of sound waves as a directional motion of the molecules superposed on their random chaotic motion, so that the energy of the sound wave is carried as kinetic energy from one gas molecule to its neighbors with which it collides. The measured wavelength of a 1000-cycle sound wave in air, at normal temperature and pressure, is 33 cm. As a rough check on the hypothesis above, show that the ratio of the rms velocity of the molecules to the velocity of the sound wave is not greater than 10.

Longitudinal waves

2-4. A longitudinal wave has the equation $y = a \sin (2\pi t/T - 2\pi x/\lambda)$. If the peak pressure associated with this wave is p_0, write the equation which gives the pressure at all points and at all times.

2-5. Draw pictures of three possible modes of vibration of a steel rod which is clamped at one end and free to move at the other.

2-6. A ship floating in still water uses echo sounding to determine the depth of the sea at a given location. Compressional wave pulses are sent to the bottom and the elapsed time between transmitted and received pulses is measured. If this elapsed time is 0.80 sec, what is the depth of the water? The bulk modulus of water is 50×10^6 lb/ft^2; weight-density of sea water = 64 lb/ft^3; acceleration of gravity = 32 ft/sec^2.

2-7. A steel rod is one meter long. The cross section of the rod is a circle whose diameter is 0.50 cm. (a) What is the velocity of longitudinal waves on this rod? (b) If the rod is clamped in the middle, what is the frequency of the fundamental mode of vibration and of the second over-tone? Young's modulus for steel = 20.0×10^{11} dynes/cm^2; density of steel = 8.0 gm/cm^3.

2-8. What is the velocity of a longitudinal wave in a platinum bar whose cross section is a rectangle with sides 0.50 cm and 1.0 cm? Young's modulus = 17×10^{11} dynes/cm^2; density is 21.4 gm/cm^3.

2-9. What is the velocity of sound in a gas whose pressure is one million dynes/cm^2, whose density is 0.00080 gm/cm^3, and for which the ratio of specific heats is 1.40?

Standing waves

2-10. A bar is supported at the middle but is free at its ends. Draw three pictures showing the amplitude of the standing wave for the first three modes of vibration.

2-11. Write the general equation for each of the following waves. Let λ = wavelength, T = period, and A = amplitude. (a) A standing wave which has nodes at $x = 0$, $\lambda/2$, etc., and which has zero amplitude at $t = 0$. (b) A progressive wave (i.e., a traveling wave) which is moving in the direction of positive x and which is zero at $x = 0$ and $t = 0$.

2-12. (a) How should a bar be clamped so that it can vibrate only at the odd harmonics? (b) If this bar is 30 in long, and if the velocity of sound in the bar is 10,000 ft/sec, what is the frequency of the fundamental and of the first overtone?

2-13. An aluminum rod 85 cm long clamped at the mid-point is used to create standing waves in a Kundt's tube experiment. If the tube is one meter long and the dust heaps accumulate at intervals of 5.5 cm, find the velocity and frequency of the sound waves in the rod. Assume the velocity of sound in air to be 330 m/sec.

2-14. A bar starts at $x = 0$ and extends along the positive x-direction. Write an equation for the amplitude of the standing wave when (a) the end at $x = 0$ is held fixed, (b) the end at $x = 0$ is free to move.

Vibrations in a string, both ends fixed

2-15. What happens to v, f, and λ as a violinist tightens a string?

2-16. Given a standing wave in a vibrating string. Discuss the use of this wave to determine the speed of the wave in the string.

2-17. Discuss the experimental methods which may be used to increase the fundamental frequency of a stretched string.

2-18. The tension in a given violin string is increased by a factor of four. What effect does this have on (a) the velocity, (b) the fundamental wavelength, (c) the fundamental frequency, of the waves in the string?

2-19. A guitar string is 2.5 ft long and has a mass of 5×10^{-5} lb/in. What is the frequency of the fundamental mode? The tension in the string is 20 lb.

2-20. A stretched wire 4.0 m long is vibrating in its fundamental mode with a maximum excursion of the center section (top to bottom) of 6.0 cm. The frequency is 5.0 vibrations/sec. (a) What is the wavelength of the waves on the wire? (b) What is the speed of the waves on the wire? (c) If the linear density of the wire is 3 gm/cm, what is the tension in the wire? (d) What is the amplitude of the component waves on the string?

2-21. A steel wire is clamped between two immovable supports 1.0 m apart. The wire has cross-sectional area 0.10 mm². When the temperature is 20 °C the wire is found to have a fundamental frequency of 100 vibrations/sec. What is the fundamental frequency when the temperature is raised to 80 °C? The density of the steel is 7.8 gm/cm³.

2-22. Standing waves are set up in a uniform rope. The rope is 3.0 m long and has a mass of 0.50 kg. The ends are fixed and the tension in the rope is 96 newtons. In this pattern three antinodes are observed. (a) Calculate the frequency of vibrations in this mode. (b) If the maximum speed of a particle in the rope at an antinode is 3.0 m/sec, what is the amplitude of the stationary wave at an antinode?

2-23. A wire 75 cm long and of mass 3.0 gm is placed under tension between rigid supports. The product of Young's modulus and the cross-sectional area of the wire (YA) is 9.0×10^9 dynes. The tension in the wire is 36×10^6 dynes. Calculate (a) the strain in the wire, (b) the velocity of propagation of transverse waves in the wire, (c) the fundamental frequency of vibration of transverse standing waves.

CHAPTER 3

Sound Waves

The *intensity* of sound is the energy per unit area per second. For direct sound from a small source, the intensity varies *inversely as the square of the distance* from the source. The intensity is proportional to the square of the amplitude:

$$I = \frac{P^2}{2\rho_0 v}. \tag{3-1}$$

Example: What must be the output of a small source of sound if the intensity 20 m away is to be 50 microwatts/cm^2? Neglect reflections.

$$A = 4\pi r^2 = 4\pi (2000 \text{ cm})^2 = 25 \times 10^6 \text{ cm}^2,$$

$$\text{power} = IA = (50 \times 10^{-6} \text{ watt/cm}^2)(25 \times 10^6 \text{ cm}^2) = 1\overline{2}5 \text{ watts}.$$

Example: If the pressure amplitude of the loudest tolerable sound is about 280 dynes cm^{-2}, what is the intensity of the sound wave?
From Eq. (3-1),

$$I = \frac{(280 \text{ cynes/cm}^2)^2}{2(0.00122 \text{ gm/cm}^3)(3.4 \times 10^4 \text{ cm/sec})} = 1\overline{0}0 \times 10^{-6} \text{ watt cm}^{-2}.$$

Intensity level β is the logarithm of the ratio of the intensity I of a sound to an arbitrarily chosen intensity I_0, usually taken as 10^{-16} watt/cm^2, approximately that of the faintest sound which can be heard. The *bel* and the *decibel* are units of intensity level. A one-bel change in intensity level represents a tenfold increase in power. In decibels,

$$\beta = 10 \log \frac{I}{I_0}. \tag{3-2}$$

Example: Two sounds of the same frequency have intensities of 10^{-13} and 10^{-16} watt/cm^2. By how much do these sounds differ in intensity level?

From Eq. (3-2),

$$\beta = 10 \log \frac{10^{-13}}{10^{-16}} = 30 \text{ db.}$$

The *loudness* of a sound is the magnitude of the auditory sensation. Sounds differ in *pitch, quality,* and *loudness.*

A musical tone is produced by a regular succession of compressions and rarefactions.

An *unpitched sound* is produced by an irregular succession of compressions and rarefactions or by a disturbance of such short duration that the ear is unable to distinguish a regular succession.

A *noise* was formerly defined as an unpitched sound; now more often noise is defined as any undesired sound.

The *pitch* of a sound is associated with the *frequency* of vibration. The average human ear is sensitive, in varying degree, to frequencies over a range of 20 to 20,000 vib/sec, as shown in the graph of the *auditory area,* Fig. 3-1.

Limits of audibility. The sensation of sound is excited only within the region of frequency and intensity enclosed by the curves of Fig. 3-1.

The *quality* of sound depends upon the *complexity* of the wave, i.e., the number and prominence of the overtones.

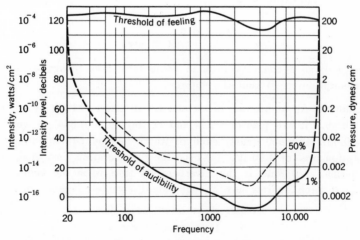

Fig. 3-1. Limits of audibility.

A *musical scale* is a succession of tones which bear a simple relation of frequencies.

Doppler's principle expresses the fact that the apparent frequency of a source of sound is changed if there is relative motion between source and observer. The apparent frequency is raised when a source moves with speed v_S toward a stationary receiver:

$$f' = \left(\frac{v_0}{v_0 - v_S}\right) f \tag{3-3a}$$

The apparent frequency f' is lowered for a receiver moving with speed v_R away from a stationary source

$$f' = \left(\frac{v_0 - v_R}{v_0}\right) f \tag{3-3b}$$

Example: A locomotive traveling at a speed of 150 ft/sec carries a whistle having a frequency of 600 cycles/sec. What is the apparent frequency of the whistle to a stationary observer in front of the train?

Take the speed of sound in air $v_0 = 1100$ ft/sec. From Eq. (3-3a),

$$f' = \frac{1100 \text{ ft/sec}}{(1100 - 150) \text{ ft/sec}} \ 600 \text{ cycles/sec} = 695 \text{ cycles/sec}.$$

Reverberation is the persistence of sound in an enclosed space, due to repeated reflections of waves. It may be reduced by sound-absorbent material in the enclosure. The approximate reverberation time of a room is given by the expression

$$T = 0.049 \ \frac{\text{volume}}{\Sigma \ \alpha \cdot \text{area}} \tag{3-4}$$

where T is in seconds, volume in cubic feet, area in square feet, and α = absorption coefficient of a surface.

Example: An auditorium is rectangular in shape, 112 ft by 68 ft, and 20 ft high. It has plaster walls and ceiling ($\alpha_1 = 0.034$), a wood floor ($\alpha_2 = 0.03$), and 550 seats, each of which has an equivalent complete absorption area of 0.10 ft². (a) Find the reverberation time of the empty auditorium. (b) What is the reverberation time when the auditorium is filled, if each auditor has an equivalent complete absorption area of 4.0 ft²?

(a) $T = 0.049 \ \dfrac{112 \times 68 \times 20}{0.034 \, (14{,}556) + 0.03 \, (7516) + 0.10 \, (550)} = 9.6$ sec,

(b) $T = 0.049 \ \dfrac{152{,}000}{0.034 \, (14{,}556) + 0.03 \, (7516) + 550 \, (4.0)} = 2.5$ sec.

Absorption occurs when the regular motion of the particles in a wave is converted into random motion (heat).

An *echo* occurs when a reflected sound wave returns to the observer 0.1 sec or longer after the original wave reaches him, so that a repetition of the original sound is perceived.

A sound wave may be *refracted* if the speed is not the same in all parts of the medium or if parts of the medium are moving. The wave may also be refracted as it passes from one medium to another.

PROBLEMS

3-1. (a) Distinguish between *loudness* of a sound and its *intensity*; between *pitch* of a sound and its *frequency*. (b) What factors enable one to distinguish between the notes emitted by a piano and a violin when both notes are of the same pitch and loudness?

Intensity; intensity level

3-2. State in words what is meant by the *intensity* of a traveling wave. Give the defining equation for the *intensity level* of a sound wave.

3-3. A sound wave has an amplitude of 1.5×10^{-6} cm and a frequency of 1000 cycles/sec. What is the intensity of this wave if the density of the gas is 0.00178 gm/cm^3 and the speed of sound is 1000 ft/sec?

3-4. A loudspeaker is supplied with power at the rate of 1000 joules/sec. At what distance from the loudspeaker will the intensity level be 50 db? State any assumptions you make.

3-5. Fill in the four missing decibel values on the scale of Fig. 3-2. You will observe that the zero of the decibel scale has been taken arbitrarily at the 10^{-8} microwatt/cm^2.

3-6. What is the intensity level of the following signals? Use a reference level of 10^{-16} watt/cm^2 and express the answer in decibels: (a) A signal whose intensity is 10^{-16} watt/cm^2. (b) A signal whose intensity is 2×10^{-14} watt/cm^2. (c) A signal whose intensity is 7.8×10^{-7} watt/cm^2.

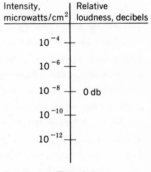

Fig. 3-2

3-7. Two sounds have intensities of 10^{-7} and 10^{-3} watt/cm^2, respectively. What is the intensity level, or loudness, of one of these sounds relative to the other?

Beats

3-8. Make a careful drawing of a 1-sec sample of two waves whose frequencies are 5 cycles/sec and 6 cycles/sec. Show how the sum varies to give a beat note. What is the frequency of the beat note?

3-9. Two tuning forks, when sounded together, produce a beat every 4 sec. The frequency of fork Y is known to be 300 vibrations/sec. When a very small bit of wax is stuck to fork X, there is a beat every 6 sec. What is the frequency of fork X?

3-10. To determine the frequency produced by a certain note on a flute, the flute note is blown and at the same time a tuning fork of standard frequency (440 cycles/sec) is struck. A beat note of frequency 4 cycles/sec is heard. Assuming the speed of sound in air to be 1100 ft/sec at 16 °C, calculate (a) the frequency of the flute note (two answers), (b) the wavelength of the sound waves in air at 16 °C produced by the tuning fork, (c) the speed of the sound waves in air at −17 °C.

3-11. How many beats per second are produced by two organ pipes, one of which is closed at both ends and the other open at one end. The lengths are L_c and L_o respectively; and the beats occur between the third harmonics of both pipes. Neglect end effects.

The ear

3-12. Discuss briefly the factors which enable one to distinguish between different sources of sound.

Doppler effect

3-13. A source of sound is vibrating with frequency 1000/sec, in still air. Arrange the following four cases in order of decreasing frequency as noted by observer when (a) the observer moves toward the stationary source with a speed v, (b) both the source and observer move with speed v in the same direction, (c) the source moves toward the stationary observer with speed v, (d) the source moves with speed v in a circle about the observer.

3-14. If a person could approach a stationary whistle of frequency f with the speed of sound, he would probably hear a sound of what frequency?

3-15. A train whistle emits sound at a frequency f_0 while the train passes point A, approaches a station S, passes the station and recedes from it past point B, always moving with a constant speed of 60 mi/hr. (a) Indicate on the graph of Fig. 3-3 (qualitatively) the frequency heard by a stationary listener at S close to the track. Include f_0 on the frequency axis. (b) On the same graph, indicate qualitatively the intensity of sound that could be measured by the listener at S as the train moves from A to B. State the manner in which the intensity of sound will be related to the distance to the train, disregarding small effects.

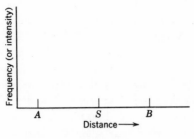

Fig. 3-3

3-16. A speeding train passes a stationary observer with the whistle blowing. The observed pitch drops from 1200 to 1000 cycles/sec. Determine the speed of the train, in miles per hour, taking the speed of sound to be 1100 ft/sec.

3-17. A man is driving 30 mi/hr along a road, with a 45 mi/hr following wind. As the car approaches a large signboard, perpendicular to the road, the driver sounds his horn, which has a frequency of 300 vib/sec. What is the frequency of the echo which the man hears?

3-18. A fighter pilot is forced to bail out and, when near the ground, his parachute catches on the limb of a tall tree. He is left hanging 60 ft below the limb, swinging in an arc of $66°25'$ each side of vertical. Directly in line with his swing is the road over which an ambulance is coming to rescue him. The ambulance is traveling 60 mi/hr and is continuously sounding a siren of frequency 1012 vibrations/sec. What frequencies does the pilot hear?

3-19. A very long freight train, with an engine at the front and a helper engine at the rear, is traveling north at 30 mi hr^{-1}. A wind is blowing south at 15 mi hr^{-1}. A car traveling north is passing the train on a road parallel to and alongside the track. When the whistles of both engines are blowing, the driver observes that he hears no beats when he is traveling 30 mi hr^{-1}; when he speeds up to 45 mi hr^{-1} he hears 10 beats/sec. What were the frequencies of each of the two train whistles?

3-20. A siren of frequency 1000 cycles/sec is located at each end of a road one mile long. With what speed must one drive along this road in order to hear a beat note of 6 cycles/sec?

3-21. You are standing at a large distance d away from a railroad track (Fig. 3-4). A train is pulling out of the station at A with constant

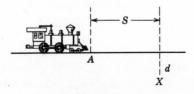

Fig. 3-4

acceleration. If S^2/d^2 is negligible compared with unity, when should the engineer on the train blow the whistle so that the frequency of the note you hear will be a maximum?

3-22. (a) An observer is at rest at the position O and a sound source S emitting at a frequency f_0 moves about him in a circular path at a constant angular velocity ω. What is the frequency of the sound heard by the observer? (b) An observer is at rest at O and a source S of frequency f_0 moves with velocity v in the direction indicated, in Fig. 3-5. What frequency does the observer hear when the source crosses the x-axis? (c) A source emitting frequency f_0 is at rest at S and an observer at O moves with velocity v in the direction indicated in Fig. 3-6. What frequency is heard by the observer as he crosses the x-axis?

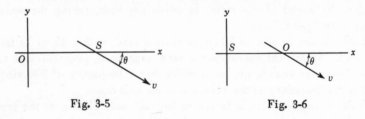

Fig. 3-5   Fig. 3-6

Reflection

3-23. The speed of sound in sea water is 4600 ft/sec. The echo of a sound sent from a ship, through the water, returns from an iceberg in 1.2 sec. Find the distance from ship to iceberg.

Reverberation

3-24. Name three factors which determine the *reverberation time* of a room.

Interference

3-25. Given two sources of sound a distance d apart (Fig. 3-7) which are emitting in time phase sound of wavelength λ. Find the points along the y-axis at which intensity minima occur.

3-26. In Fig. 3-8, a tube of cross section A splits into two tubes, each of cross section $A/2$. The branches are of lengths 2.0 ft and 3.0 ft, respectively; they rejoin to form again a tube of cross section A. By

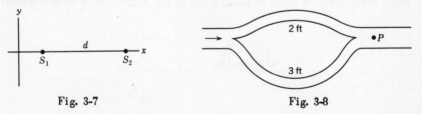

Fig. 3-7   Fig. 3-8

considering what happens at point P, describe what happens to sound sent down the tube from the left, of frequency (a) 1000 cycles/sec, and (b) 500 cycles/sec.

3-27. A microphone has an electrical output e which is given by $e = ap + bp^2$, where a and b are constants and p is the pressure of the incident wave. List all of the frequencies that would be found in the output when two waves of frequencies 1000 and 3000 cycles/sec arrive at the microphone simultaneously.

3-28. A sound wave whose frequency is 1000 cycles/sec is received on a microphone whose response is given by $e = ap + bp^2$. What frequencies are present in the output of the microphone? Is a dc voltage present in the output?

Sound

PART A

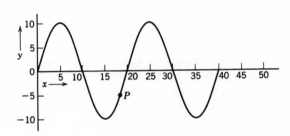

Fig. 1

The graph of Fig. 1 represents a "snapshot" of a wave traveling in the positive x-direction from a source vibrating with a frequency of 100 cycles/sec. Use this information to answer Questions 1 to 5:

1. What is the wavelength?
2. What is the amplitude?
3. What is the period?
4. What is the velocity with which the disturbance is traveling?
5. What is the displacement of a particle at P the instant we view it?
6. The projection in a horizontal plane of a point moving with uniform circular motion in a vertical circle is called (A) transverse vibrations, (B) longitudinal vibrations, (C) simple harmonic motion, (D) complex vibrations.
7. The motion of a particle moving along a line which is the direction of propagation of the wave is called (A) transverse vibrations, (B) longitudinal vibrations, (C) simple harmonic motion, (D) complex vibrations.
8. Two waves of the same frequency, traveling in the same medium but in opposite directions, give rise to the phenomena of (A) beats, (B) resonance, (C) standing waves, (D) overtones, (E) harmonics.
9. One vibrating object can cause another which is nearby also to vibrate if they both have the same natural frequency. This effect is commonly referred to as (A) beats, (B) resonance, (C) standing waves, (D) overtones, (E) harmonics.

10. Which of the following affects the speed with which sound travels in a medium: (A) pressure, (B) frequency of the sound, (C) density of the material, (D) none of these?

11. What physical property or properties of sound waves correspond to what musicians call quality or timbre?

12. What physical property or properties of sounds correspond to what, in music, is called pitch?

13. What distinguishes noise from musical sounds?

14. The highest frequency the human ear is capable of hearing is about (A) 5000, (B) 10,000, (C) 20,000, (D) 50,000, (E) 100,000 cycles/sec.

15. Lissajous figures are useful in comparing (A) frequency, (B) loudness, (C) quality.

16. Define *intensity* as applied to sounds.

17. What unit is used to compare intensities?

18. Why is loudness measured on a logarithmic scale?

19. Under what conditions are waves reflected?

20. What would you suggest, in general, as a cure for a room which had a reverberation time too long for good speech intelligibility?

21. What is a necessary condition that two musical sounds shall sound harmonious?

22. How would the apparent frequency compare with the real frequency of a stationary object emitting sound if I were to approach it at the speed of sound?

23. What simultaneous requirements make construction of a musical scale difficult?

24. Under what conditions does sound sometimes not follow a straight path, causing freak good or poor hearing at certain distances?

PART B

1. Suppose you see a flash of lightning and hear the sound of thunder 3.0 sec later. If the air temperature is 15°C, how far away was the lightning flash?

2. Suppose ordinary speech to be sound of about 200 cycles/sec. Find the length of these waves.

3. A man is using a standard source of sound at 264 cycles/sec to tune a string of a stringed instrument to this frequency. When he sounds the two sources at the same time, he hears 5 beats/sec. After tightening the string, he hears 2 beats/sec. What was the frequency of the string before this adjustment?

4. How long should a closed organ pipe be to be used as low C, 132 cycles/sec?

5. A string is driven with a fork at 120 cycles/sec. The tension is so adjusted that we observe standing waves traveling 2400 cm/sec down the string. How far is it between nodes?

6. If one sound is 60 db louder than another, what are their relative energies?

7. What will be frequency of the sound heard by pedestrians from an auto horn of 200 vib/sec if the car is traveling toward the pedestrians at a speed of 88 ft/sec?

Sound

Sample Examination (50 min)

1. A body of mass 1000 gm is suspended by a steel wire 50.0 cm long which has a mass of 9.80×10^{-3} gm/cm. (a) If the wire is made to vibrate, what will be the fundamental frequency? (b) What mass must be added to the 1000 gm to change the fundamental frequency by 1.0 cycle/sec?

2. The displacement of the air molecules in an open pipe of length 60.0 cm is given as a function of position x and time t by the following expression:

$$y = y_0 \cos \frac{\pi x}{20} \sin 1600 \pi t,$$

where x is measured from the end of the tube. (a) What is the wavelength of the vibration? (b) Is it a traveling or a standing wave? (c) What is the speed of sound in this medium? (d) Is this vibration one of the harmonics of the tube? If so, which? (e) If y_0 is increased by a factor of 10, by how many decibels does the loudness increase? (f) How many pressure nodes are present in the tube?

3. What is the wavelength of the sound emitted by a closed organ pipe of length 10.0 cm vibrating in its fundamental mode? (b) If the air in the tube is replaced by helium gas at the same temperature, how is the wavelength of the fundamental affected? (c) the frequency? (d) the kinetic energy of the gas molecules? (e) the velocity?

4. A train blowing a whistle is approaching a mountain directly ahead; and the engineer hears a beat tone of 80 cycles/sec between the notes of the whistle (320 cycles/sec at rest) and its echo from the mountain. (a) Which sound is of higher frequency, whistle or echo? (b) What is the speed of the train? (c) What would be the frequency of the beat tone if there were a tail wind blowing at 40 ft/sec?

Index

(Page numbers in parentheses refer to numerical problems.)